Harry A. Sisson

Books by H. Allen Smith

MR. KLEIN'S KAMPF

LOW MAN ON A TOTEM POLE

LIFE IN A PUTTY KNIFE FACTORY

LOST IN THE HORSE LATITUDES

RHUBARB

LO, THE FORMER EGYPTIAN!

LARKS IN THE POPCORN

WE WENT THATAWAY

PEOPLE NAMED SMITH

MISTER ZIP

SMITH'S LONDON JOURNAL

THE COMPLEAT PRACTICAL JOKER

THE REBEL YELL

THE AGE OF THE TAIL

Selected by H. Allen Smith

DESERT ISLAND DECAMERON

With Ira L. Smith

LOW AND INSIDE

THREE MEN ON THIRD

The Age of the Tail

H. ALLEN SMITH

The Age
of the
TAIL

ILLUSTRATED BY
LEO HERSHFIELD

Boston · Little, Brown and Company · *Toronto*

*Published simultaneously in Canada
by Little, Brown & Company (Canada) Limited*

PRINTED IN THE UNITED STATES OF AMERICA

Foreword

ONE SUMMER afternoon in 1954 a few people were sitting around a swimming pool in a suburb north of New York. Among them was Marie Michau, an attractive lady out of South Africa. She sat watching two men who were cavorting in the water and after a while she spoke.

"I've often wondered," she said, "what it would be like if people had tails."

"Tails?" someone repeated. "How do you mean, tails?"

"Long, bushy tails," she said. "If we all had long, bushy tails, think how it would change the way we dress. And think of all the new things that would come along. Tail jewelry, for example."

At the moment nobody seemed to give much serious thought to the proposition. Certainly Miss Michau had no way of knowing that within three years her idle speculation would acquire the light of prophecy. Nor could she foretell that long afterward this modest history would be undertaken to show how conservative her prophetic judgment had been.

Contents

The Age of the Tail

I

The New Member

In the beginning years all sorts of theories were advanced to explain it. The most reliable men of science could interpret it only as an abrupt reversal of the process of evolution. They surmised that history was doubling back on its long track and that in a mere hundred thousand years or so, mankind would once again be living in trees, minus his opposable thumb and minus laughter. The masses refused to accept this idea of retrogression, however, and scoffed at the notion that human beings are destined to end up where they started — as blobs of jelly floating in the sea. Popular opinion was divided between those who blamed the whole thing on nuclear experiments conducted during the 1950's, and those who saw in it the workings of Divine Providence. The latter, of course, were in the majority.

It began, as we all know, at a precise moment in

history — on the twenty-second of September in the year 1957 at five thirty-five o'clock in the morning (Eastern daylight-saving time) . From that moment on every child born into the world was equipped with a tail.

This brief history of the coming of the tail is being composed in the winter of 1997–1998, just forty years after the fact. Let it be said now that in the opinion of this historian (and in the opinion of most social historians) there is no appreciable evidence today to support the theory that man is moving backwards into antiquity and beyond. So far as any student of human behavior can ascertain, people are the same today as they were in the summer of 1957, except for their tails and except for those changes in manners and morals that have been wrought by the tail.

Yet it has been a long and difficult period of transition — a period that has by no means ended. We live today in a world where all human beings over forty years of age are tailless; where the human tail is accepted and even gloried in — a far cry from those early days of shame and conceit and humiliation; and yet a world where certain minority groups abase the tail as a punishment from God, while other groups hide it away or cut it off in the belief

[4]

... men of science could interpret it only as an abrupt reversal of the process of evolution ..

that it is an affliction placed upon the human race by Satan himself.

Let us consider the tail as a physical phenomenon. Prior to 1957 it was known, of course, that the human embryo produced an external jointed tail in the fifth week of its development in the womb. By the eighth week this tail had shriveled up and disappeared into a dimple. There were occasional exceptions — cases in which babies were born with their tails intact. Medical men referred to these appendages as "soft tails" for the reason that they were composed of muscles, nerves, and blood vessels, without vertebrae. They were quite similar to the tail of the Barbary ape and were usually about six inches in length at birth. Children born with them were known as "soft tail sports" and as a general rule the flabby projection was snipped off and forgotten (it was looked upon as a freak of nature, the same as an extra toe). In some of the more backward portions of the world, such as China, certain sections of the city of Baltimore, and the border counties of Texas, soft tails were found on children twelve years of age or older.

The tail that arrived and became universal in the fall of '57, however, was notable for its vertebrae. Medical science now knows almost all there is to

know about the human tail and in recent years there
have been many learned and technical papers issued
on the anatomical structure of the tail, on tail ailments, tail surgery, and tail hygiene, among other
subjects. The human tail as we know it today bears
a close physical kinship to the tail of a cat, a dog,
a cow, or a monkey. From a length of five or six
inches at birth it grows to slightly over three feet
at maturity, and it contains from twenty to thirty
vertebrae. The muscular system is quite complex,
especially around the sacrum, where the dorsalis
serves to raise the tail, the ventralis lowers it, and
the lateralis muscles move it from side to side. These
tail muscles are well developed in most individuals
largely because of the stresses and strains put upon
them by the requirements of modern social life and
the dictates of fads, fashions, and general etiquette.

The hair covering of the human tail differs in
individuals and this fact is of the utmost importance
when we come to consider its sociological implications. As a general thing the female tail resembles
that of a collie and the long-growing hair is soft and
silky, either by nature or from persistent grooming.*

* The basic differences between the female tail and the male
tail have been a matter for study and speculation for many
years. In 1953, Professor Ashley Montagu of Princeton, writing to *The Saturday Review*, sought to correct "a long-stand-

The New Member

In the male the tail hair grows much the way his beard grows and is often coarse and ungovernable. In its natural state, tail hair is almost always the same color as the hair on the individual's head, and turns gray at the same time.

The skin beneath the hair covering of the human tail is a grayish pink, so that a shaved tail or a bald tail lacks beauty and, in fact, is regarded by people of squeamish disposition as a revolting sight.

In the last forty years (actually the last twenty) this supple extension of the spinal column has brought radical changes in man's way of life, his general behavior, and his personality. Man has been able to accomplish a great deal more with his tail than a dog or a cat or even a monkey might accomplish for the reason that man is a thinking animal. As Dr. Hugh Dewhirst put it: "Awareness is the significant point. A dog doesn't know it has a tail.

---

ing error" — the belief that Eve was created from a spare rib of Adam. Professor Montagu argued: "Every student of anatomy knows that the number of ribs in each sex is identical. Woman couldn't, therefore, have been created from a spare rib of the male — the evidence of human and comparative anatomy is entirely contrary to such a suggestion. The evidence, on the other hand, indicates that the male was created from one of the female's spare parts, namely, one of her coccygeal, or tail, vertebrae, for, on the average, women have only three coccygeal vertebrae whereas men have four."

It is back there and it is extraordinarily active, but the dog is not aware of it and never gives it a thought. If the dog *knew* it had a tail, it might be able to do something useful with it."

What man has done with, and because of, his new member is the principal concern of this outline.

I I

Time of Confusion
and Shame

Acquisition of a tail gave man his greatest shock
since that medieval day when he first learned that
his planet was not the center of the universe, and at
the very beginning he refused to accept it. During
those first few days in September of '57 the tails
of most newborn infants were amputated, just as
"soft tails" had been amputated in the past. The
medical men, however, realized that an important
anatomical change had occurred. They knew very
little about vertebrated tails and so, with some reluctance, they turned to the veterinarians for coun-
sel.

The docking of the tails of certain breeds of dogs
was common practice and the operation was usually performed by the veterinarian (or by the dog
owner) within a few days of birth, at which time
the puppy suffered little or no pain. Where the am-

putation was delayed a matter of weeks it became a more serious matter and the tail had to be anesthetized.

The medical men could see no great point in cutting off a baby's tail and leaving a stub three or four inches long. And they had found that removal of the human tail at the base was somewhat more than a minor operation. Within a very short time, then, the doctors concluded that the tail should stay. In many cases the parents of newborn babes overruled them and demanded complete amputation, and since medical opinion was slow in crystallizing, since it had little in the way of precedent to guide it, most doctors complied.

The remarkable thing about it was the secrecy, or, rather, the pretense of secrecy. Babies with tails were being born by the thousand, yet there was no whisper of the fact in the press. The entire nation, in those first days, was bewildered and frightened, and almost by common consent nothing was said about the phenomenon publicly. Everyone knew about it and whispered about it, but the confusion and worry was so great that the newspapers and radio and television held back.

The government in Washington encouraged, for the moment, this national "secret." The situation

The docking of the tail of certain breeds
of dogs was a common practice...

was considered to be extremely grave because someone in the State Department had suggested that the
tail had come to the people of the United States
and not to the people of other nations. There was
no word from our representatives abroad to indicate
that foreign babies were being born with tails, and
Washington statesmen foresaw the blackest of dif-
ficulties if it were true. Our enemies, upon learning
that we were turning into a tailed race, would have
no trouble uniting the entire tailless world against
us. People without tails would not tolerate people
with tails, and the rest of the world would form a
sort of holy crusade to exterminate us.

The State Department sent urgent queries to its
representatives abroad. The President stayed at his
desk late every night, deeply concerned over the
international implications of the problem. Then
during the evening of October 1, nine days after
the first tails appeared, the secret dispatches began
coming in. Our diplomats, adhering to the basic
precepts of their calling, had taken their time, re-
fusing to commit themselves until they were doubly
sure of their ground. One by one their messages were
decoded and laid before the President. Most of them
said, simply, "Tails here." By nine o'clock that evening the government was convinced that babies in

Asia and Europe and Australia and Africa and Tierra del Fuego were being born with tails.

The President quickly decided that the nation's press should "apprise the people of the truth" on the following morning. He prepared his own announcement for release to morning newspapers and signed it in the presence of several dignitaries, using seven different fountain pens which were presented as souvenirs to the heads of the three wire services, a representative of the Society for the Prevention of Cruelty to Children, and the presidents of the American Medical Association, the American Eugenics Association, and the American Veterinary Medical Association.

So it was that on the morning of September 25 the nation's newspapers carried screaming headlines to tell a story that everyone already knew. The television and radio commentators talked about nothing else throughout that day, interviewing scientists, doctors, clergymen, veterinarians, men-in-the-street, cat fanciers, advertising executives . . . anyone they could grab and get to talking on the subject of tails. Our older citizens remember the wild tempestuousness of that day and enjoy recalling many of the things that happened, many of the things that were said. They remember the front page of

Time of Confusion and Shame

the New York tabloid which proclaimed in boxcar type:

ALL GOD'S
CHILLUN
GOT TAILS!

They remember the man-in-the-street interviews conducted throughout the day by CBS-TV. A transcript of one such interview follows:

ANNOUNCER: We are now at the busy intersection of Fifth Avenue and Forty-ninth Street. Ah, here's an intelligent-looking citizen. Pardon me, sir. Could you tell us your name?

MAN IN STREET: Senga J. Simms.

ANNOUNCER: Senga . . . that's an unusual name, isn't it?

MAN IN STREET: I don't see nothing so unusual about it. It's my mother's name spelled backwards. Agnes spelled backwards.

ANNOUNCER: Oh, I see. That's real nice. It's a pleasant thing nowadays to meet a man who is a living tribute to his mother.

MAN IN STREET: I ain't. Oney my name is.

ANNOUNCER: Well, Mr. Simms, today we are asking the man-in-the-street a question about tails. Would you care to answer that question for our TV audience?

MAN IN STREET: What question?

ANNOUNCER: I haven't asked it yet.

MAN IN STREET: I know you ain't ast it yet. But I got to know what it is before I can decide if I'm gonna answer it, don't I? Ast it.

[17]

The Age of the Tail

ANNOUNCER: The question is — what do you think will happen to tails in the future?

MAN IN STREET: Tails? What tails?

ANNOUNCER: You know, the tails that all the babies are being born with now.

MAN IN STREET: Oh, them tails! You want I should give my opinion whether they got any future?

ANNOUNCER: Well . . . yes.

MAN IN STREET: You don't see no tail hangin' on me, do you?

ANNOUNCER: No, of course not.

MAN IN STREET: Then why you astin' me? Why don't you go talk to somebody's got a tail? Like maybe a horse. Haw haw haw haw! Hey, all you fellas at Mickey's Bar & Grill, how'd ya like that one?

ANNOUNCER: Please, Mr. Simms. Have you no ideas at all about what we should do with our tails?

MAN IN STREET: I got one idea — what you can do with yours — oney it ain't practical, and furthermore . . .

(*Music up and over*)

There was, also, the appearance that same evening of Miss Tee Tee Frid, beautiful young newcomer to the films. Miss Frid was interviewed on the Betty Nibben TV show. A brief excerpt from the transcript follows:

MISS NIBBEN: Now, Miss Frid, I wanted to ask you . . .

MISS FRID: My latest pictyure is *Redheads Are Dangerous*. It is a kind of doccamentary, and in it I play the part of . . .

Time of Confusion and Shame

MISS NIBBEN: One moment, Miss Frid. I wanted to ask you an important question, a question that is in everybody's mind these days. Just what do you think of all this tail talk?

MISS FRID: I don't go in for gossip.

It seems strange at this date to reflect on the violence of the controversies which arose in those first months. Scientists quarreled with scientists, doctors fought doctors, religious leaders disagreed with other religious leaders, politicians scarified fellow politicians, and the ordinary citizen was left with his brain awhirl. He knew only one thing for certain: all new babies had tails. He heard loud and anguished cries emanating from Southern California and the Middle West, where leaders of minor religious cults were shrieking their own interpretations of the situation, which they all regarded as calamitous. An evangelistic spellbinder in Ohio made the greatest noise and attracted the greatest following by proclaiming that the "Merlins of Hell" had taken over human biology, that Satan himself had fastened his tail upon the human race and his next move would be at the other end — he would transfer his malefic brain to man. More liberal-minded clergymen tried to reassure the people, pointing out that if Satan *had* given man his tail,

[19]

the tail would be forked. "It'll be forked in time!" cried the Ohio evangelist in rebuttal. A committee of college professors, alarmed over the progress of the Satan theory, issued a statement questioning the existence of Satan. "If he did exist," the statement said, "he would not likely have a tail, forked or otherwise. The popular conception of Satan as having horns and cloven hooves and a forked tail was borrowed from the image of the pagan god, Pan."

Meanwhile, tail amputations continued in the hospitals, even though almost all doctors inveighed against the practice. The parents of many newborn babies argued: "It's all very well for you to sit there and say that tails are okay, and maybe a good thing. But wait till your own child is born with one. *Then* you'll change your tune!" And so many of them demanded that the tails be hacked off, a decision most of them would live to regret.

The sentiment in favor of retaining tails, however, grew swiftly with the support of medical organizations and other scientific groups who contended that to sever a tail was to violate natural law. Certain elements of the clergy joined the movement, holding that tail amputation was an insult to the Deity.

In this atmosphere one reputable newspaper appealed to the public to use "plain everyday horse sense" in resolving the question.

"Let us all be calm," this newspaper urged, "and handle the question rationally. After all, these tails may drop off our babies after a few months."

But the tails didn't drop off.

In fact they were beginning to grow. And they were beginning to grow hair.

When the first tail babies had reached the age of three, their tails were about nine inches long. At the age of five they were eleven inches long, and growing fast.

As the tails increased in size, there was a corresponding increase in the discomfort to their owners, for they were kept hidden beneath diapers and play suits. Just as in the case of young dogs, children were inclined to wag their tails almost constantly, and having them trussed up within their rompers proved not only uncomfortable but downright painful. The first cases of wry tail, or *tail torticollis*, were reported.

It was not until 1965 that the psychologists prevailed, with the support of the medical profession, and the human tail was brought out into the open. By this time eight-year-old children had tails eighteen inches long and well haired.

The Age of the Tail

The first people affected commercially (not counting the doctors and not including the evangelists) were the stylists who design clothing for children. Up to this point they had been devising various bags and hammocks and even small bustles for containing the tail inside the clothing. The most sensible of these early designs was that of a loose-fitting tail case, extending up the child's back; it gave the tail a certain amount of play so stiffness wouldn't develop, and it got the tail out of the way so that the child would not hurt himself whenever he sat down.

With the emergence of tails from their prison, the designers experimented with various folds and drapes and even zipper openings, seeking the total emancipation of the tail without offending normal human modesty. It remained for a French expatriate, M. Pierre Sansone, to arrive at the obvious solution: a round hole in the seat of the pants (or the frock). At first this hole was simply hemstitched. It was soon found that because of the immense vigor of a child's tail, something more durable was needed, and the evolution of the tail collar began — the edging of the hole with, first, more durable fabrics and, second, more attractive materials. The day of the resplendent tail collar and the bejeweled tail choker, however, was still some distance in the future.

I I I

The Murchison Theory

PRESIDENT HUNT MURCHISON, who was recognized as one of the world's foremost biochemists before his election to the White House in 1996, was born in 1952 without a tail. Yet this fine man, operating in a field somewhat removed from the range of his special training, worked out the celebrated Theory of Caudal Dynamics. It is said that only eight living men have a full understanding of the Murchison Theory, although its principal points may be summarized as follows:

1. The chief curse of the human race, before the coming of the tail, was nervousness. This universal nervousness was responsible for wars, stock-market fluctuations, unhappy marriages, juvenile delinquency, inadequate price supports for farm products, the resurgence of the labor unions, and the common cold.

2. The American nation, leading the world in all

other fields of human achievement, also led the world in nervousness.

3. The causation of nervousness is wrapped up in the problem of controlling emotional thought. Once the emotions are effectually in leash, all nervousness vanishes. (Here is one point at which Murchison struck out boldly for himself.)

4. The human tail, insofar as emotions are concerned, is a semaphore, a barometer, a yardstick. Up until the arrival of the tail, people for the most part were able to conceal their emotions. (If the hinder parts of a dog are hidden in a box, said Murchison, we are unable to tell whether that dog is happy or sad, alert or relaxed, sated or hungry.)

5. Fifteen years after the arrival of the caudal appendage, the necessity for rigid tail control became apparent. Strict training, from earliest childhood, and the exercise of the most intense will power were required if a person hoped to hide his true feelings from the world.

6. In the past our educational system provided no adequate method for the control and manipulation of will power. As early as 1970, however, our elementary schools were devoting a great deal of attention to the tail and its management. During the

intervening years this program has been intensified, with the consequence that certain areas of the brain have been affected in a salutary way. The race is acquiring a self-control never known before in history. As self-control has moved steadily upward on the graph, nervousness has gone into a corresponding decline. Before long, nervousness will disappear entirely, and with it will disappear wars, stock-market fluctuations, unhappy marriages, juvenile delinquency, inadequate price supports for farm products, the resurgence of the labor unions, and the common cold.

Thus a simplified statement of the Murchison Theory. It is taken in part from the analysis made by Dr. Orville Opsott, the popular psychologist.*

Dr. Opsott has given us a vivid picture of the changes that have come about in our schoolrooms. He notes with tolerant irony that in 1965, when the tails of children were first brought outside the clothing, there was considerable confusion in the schools. The coming revolution in furniture design had its beginnings in those classrooms. Three-inch holes were drilled in the wooden seats and the pupil was

* Author of the book *The Power of a Positive Tail,* which has been a best seller since its publication in 1991.

required, after the standing Pledge to the Flag, to poke his tail into this hole and then sit in the same position for half an hour. If he tried to shift himself about on the seat, he would likely injure his tail muscles or even dislocate some of the vertebrae. Every thirty minutes the teacher would call Tail Recess, a period of three minutes in which the pupil stood beside his desk and wagged his tail vigorously to freshen circulation and get the stiffness out of it.

The attitude of the children at this point was a problem. They saw in the tail merely something to pull. A pulled tail, as we all know, is quite a painful matter, especially among tender-tailed children. At first it was almost more than the teachers could cope with. Little girls as well as little boys, sitting in fixed positions at their desks, bored by their inability to squirm and fidget, often were unable to get their minds off the fact that the tail of the pupil in front of them was dangling within easy reach. And sometimes the tykes could not resist the urge to reach down and give the tail a hearty pull. This always brought yelps of pain from the boys and shrill screeches from the girls and then punishment for the culprit — he was usually compelled to stand in a corner with a half-pound lead weight fastened to

[26]

his tail for fifteen minutes, an agonizing experience if we are to believe those who suffered it.

In time, as Dr. Opsott points out, child psychologists worked out methods for implanting in the juvenile mind a healthy respect for the tails of others, so that today tail pulling in school is no longer commonplace. Children had to be taught convincingly that their tails were important and not mere playthings, and this was achieved through certain psychological devices and through the introduction of basic tail training into the curriculum.

The purpose of this training, required of every child possessing a sound tail, is twofold. First, it is important that the human tail be strong and supple and well groomed if its owner hopes to make his mark in life; and, second, it is even more important that a person know how to fake effectively with his tail. The ability to dissemble has long been one of the first requirements for success in business and politics as well as in social life. Many important business executives nowadays employ tail watchers — people who are skilled in the art of detecting the meaning of the slightest tremor in a tail. Some executives have secretaries who are expert at "reading" tails, while others have full-length mirrors in their offices, by means of which they are able to study the tail movements of persons being interviewed. Personnel managers, who formerly paid particular attention to the manner in which an applicant shifted his eyes, now concentrate their attention on his tail. Unless the applicant has been properly trained in the art of dissembling, his tail is almost certain to give him away when he utters an untruth. If he has full control over his tail, he can convince others that he is able and ambitious and honest; if he doesn't have that control, he very likely will reveal weaknesses in his character.

Out of these needs, and out of those early groping experiments, came the over-all educational program involving the tail. Arithmetic and spelling were de-emphasized in order that more time could be given to the new subject. Beginning in the earliest grades children were indoctrinated in the Code of the Tail. The final forms of tail etiquette were beginning to take shape. It is interesting to look back at some of the first charts that were used in our public schools. They were designed to teach the meaning of the various tail positions and tail movements. For example, a loose tail, hanging straight downward, denoted either complete relaxation or humility. A tail curled inward between the legs was the symbol of shame. Other standard tail postures included:

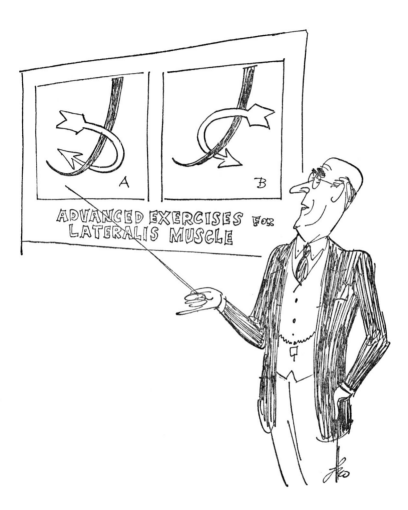

...taught in high school and college...

The Murchison Theory

Pendant, but swinging slowly from side to side:	*contentment*
Slightly stiffened and extended outward a few inches:	*mild alarm or concern*
Straight out from the body:	*commendable pride*
Curled tip:	*chagrin, disappointment*
Upright and bristling:	*belligerency, patriotism*
Upright and quivering (known as the "gay" position):	*passion, desire*
Akimbo, or curved outward:	*sorrow*
Rotating rapidly, clockwise:	*extreme happiness*
Rotating rapidly, counterclockwise:	*conceit*

These were and still are the natural, involuntary tail reactions to emotional stimuli, and these were the basic positions and maneuvers employed in the tail calisthenics classes. It must be noted, however, that the two whirling, or rotating, movements were not taught until high school and college, being too difficult for children whose lateralis muscles were not fully developed.

The earliest tail calisthenics were conducted outdoors, in the schoolyard, much as they are today, with the instructor standing on a platform and the children lined up, tails toward him. It is always a stirring sight (as we view it today) to see the orderly ranks of children going through their exercises while the instructor barks his orders into a microphone: "Tails up! Tails down! Tails akimbo! Tails right! Tails left! Tails out! Curl your tips! Tails at ease!" Yet in those days many adults considered these exercises to be comical, and when the hour came for tail calisthenics at a given school, people from all over the neighborhood congregated at the fences, sometimes in the hundreds, and, demonstrating extremely rude taste, howled and shrieked with laughter until the commands of the instructor could not be heard. The onlookers even shouted their own orders at the children, such as, "Tails in yer hip pocket!" or "Tails ahoy!" or even "Bite off the ends!" So it was that the exercises were moved indoors, away from the gaze of boorish grownups.

Let us pay tribute to those early instructors. They stuck to the job, inculcating in our children a respect for the importance of the tail and a knowledge of tail faking that would serve them well in later life. One of the things the calisthenics instructors continually emphasized to the children was this:

"You've got to pretend that part of your brain is in your tail — that you almost *think* with your tail."

As we know today, that has always been good, sound, solid advice.

I V

Minervas and Maxes

DURING the latter half of the present century certain French critics have adopted the contumelious practice of referring to the American people as *les moutons*. We are likened to sheep because of the alacrity with which we take to current fads and fancies.

There may be some small justification for the charge that we are a nation of conformists, although we don't have to hear it from these Parisian pollywogs; the matter has been considered by a few of our own writers. The late Purvis Jack, known as the Sage of Waccabuc, touched on this very question in his memoirs, published in 1968. Mr. Jack dealt with what he called the American proclivity for "overdoing a good thing," and he cited a number of illustrations out of his own experience.

He could remember when the selection of "Miss America" in the Atlantic City Beauty Pageant each year was an event commanding almost as much attention as the World Series; yet by the 1940s there were so many competing beauty pageants that "Miss America" attracted little more notice than the beer queens of the various large cities, or such other beauties as Miss Freight Forwarder, Miss Elbow Macaroni, Miss Aluminum Stepladder, Miss Illinois Cemetery Association, or Miss Athletic Supporter.

Mr. Jack recalled a time when the Pulitzer Prizes in Literature were a big thing, an annual sensation in the world of letters; yet by the 1940s there were so many other major literary awards that the Pulitzer selections were all but lost in the shuffle.

The Waccabuc philosopher looked back to the time when the Rose Bowl game in California was *THE* football event of the year, and he saw the arrival of competing games in bowls called Sugar, Cotton, Dill Pickle, Tangerine, Shrimp, Refrigerator, Turpentine, Gator, Oil, Orange, Alphabet Soup, Sun, Vulcan, Borsht, and others.*

Mr. Jack was an astringent writer. Carrying his point a step further he said:

When I was a child, a doll was a doll and its chief function was to hold still while its costume was being changed. Then came the doll that opened and closed its eyes, fol-

---

* The effect the tail has had on the game of football will be considered later in this work.

lowed by the doll that whined "Mama" in a tinny voice. There was no stopping the dollmakers after that. Before long we had dolls that wet their diapers, dolls that blew their noses, dolls that knelt to say their prayers, dolls that drooled and dolls that burped. Now, of course, all dolls have tails which begin wagging when a command is spoken. The day is not far off, I am sure, when we shall have dolls that live as man and wife.

Mr. Jack, we suspect, wrote with tongue in cheek. But not so the European critics. Today they are accusing us of "overdoing" on tails.

It must be admitted that the Europeans have, by and large, grown their tails and gone about their business. They have been slow to take up the fads and fashions that have been prevalent from time to time in the United States. The British, for example, all but ignore their own tails. The French have been a little less stolid and indifferent. American tourists are sometimes amused to see a Frenchman, upon being introduced to a lady, seize her tail and, bending from the waist, bestow a fervent kiss on it. The importance of the tail as a seat of affection is also openly recognized in Italy, where young lovers commonly walk along the streets holding tails — an activity that is frowned upon in our country.

We need make no defense against these foreign critics. Let it be said, however, that the American enthusiasm for tails represents the American enthusiasm for life and all its adjuncts and appurtenances. We have *done things* with our tails; we enjoy the possession of them; and we get the most possible pleasure out of them.

As suggested earlier in these pages, it was not always so. It took strong argument and an intensive educational campaign to convince the American public that tails could be a good thing. It took stronger argument to bring the tails out into the open. It is worth recalling that in those early days the arguments of men who were dead and gone before the arrival of the tail were employed to convert people to tails.

For example, wide circulation was given to a quotation from the works of the British writer H. G. Wells. Mr. Wells, concerned with organic evolution, noted that the tail was the instrument by which marine creatures first managed to move themselves about in the water — a major step in the direction of life on the land. He wrote:

Nowadays, we human beings, like the fox in the fable, are inclined to find tails disgraceful and to think it ignominious that we should possess such appendages even in unconscious embryohood; but let us not forget that our stock swam to supremacy before the fingered limb had

...in Italy young lovers commonly walk along the streets holding tails...

been invented. In a very real sense it was our tails that made us what we are.

Wide circulation also was given to a bit of verse composed by one Peleg Arkwright many years before the coming of the tail. It follows:

> Nature abhors imperfect work
> And on it lays her ban;
> And all creation must despise
> A tailless man.

Such observations out of the past were employed in the over-all propaganda campaign through which the American public was finally sold on tails. And while a great majority of the people did come to accept them, certain individuals and certain groups of individuals still entertained misgivings.

The fact that the human tail, in the female, is a sensitive erogenous zone did not come to full public attention until the middle '70s, perhaps for the reason that we were concerned with more practical matters up to that time. It must also be kept in mind that the erogenous characteristic was not considered important until the first tail wearers had reached their late teens. But the moment the subject came before the public, there was an immediate outcry from groups of older women whose lingering prudery was shocked. An organization was formed dedicated to the task of convincing all American women that the female tail should not be visible in public. This group refused to employ the word "erogenous" and referred to the tail as "the zone." These misguided women neglected the fact that females are equipped with more than several erogenous zones, among them the lips, the palm of the hand, the lobule of the ear, and even the little finger. Their movement, on the whole, was a ridiculous one and has never progressed any further than Calendar Reform, Simplified Spelling, or the split-level doghouse.

On the other hand, a larger group of women, acting through some ingrained sense of puritanism, rebelled against calling a tail a tail. The word itself had somehow come to have a salacious connotation to them, and their revolt against it recalled the moral atmosphere prevailing at the beginning of the century. In those times proper people, especially ladies, never used the word "leg" and it is on record that in 1900 at a chicken dinner in a Philadelphia home, one lady solemnly said she would take "a limb" while another said she preferred "the bosom."

The matter of renaming the tail was one of the principal questions up for discussion at the 1974 convention of the American Federation of Women's Clubs. The leaders of the federation made it clear that they had no quarrel with tails themselves, that they were not trying to hide them away; they simply thought the name possessed overtones of vulgarity and they proposed to do something about it. It was decided that the membership of the federation should join in a national contest to select a substitute name for the tail, first prize to be a set of guided missiles for the home.

During the ensuing months thousands of women submitted names to the contest committee. The best of these suggestions were weeded out and laid before the board of judges, whose honorary chairman was the President of the United States.*

This final list included the following:

Willow	Muff	Trail	Pendant
Serpentine	Caudette	Branch	Whip
Baton	Wiggler	Clarinette	Stalk
Tassel	Muskette	Twig	Tippet
Queue	Dong	Penduline	Brake Rod

The winner was not among these. A Mrs. Merriwether Frode of Logansport, Indiana, was awarded the grand prize. She had suggested that the tail of

* The President accepted the honorary chairmanship, smiling into the cameras during a ceremony on the White House lawn. Some years later it was revealed that, immediately after the ceremony, the President said to his press aide: "Goddammit, Purdy, why do I always have to get sucked into things like this?"

the female should be called a "Minerva" and that of the male a "Max."

When the judges had made their decision, the federation called upon its entire membership, and upon all other American citizens of good will, henceforth to refrain from ever calling a tail a tail, but to call it either a Minerva or a Max.

This movement made a little headway. Advertisers were prevailed upon to speak of Minervas and Maxes. Some newspapers took it up, and it might have succeeded but for a motion-picture hero named Wyatt Vance. Mr. Vance upset the tail cart.

In the spring of 1975, when the Minerva-Max campaign was in full blossom, Twentieth Century-Paramount released a comedy romance titled *It Happened Twice One Night*. Stars of the picture were the currently favored screen lovers Wyatt Vance and Imodell Parrish. To the young people of America, these two were as god and goddess, and each film they made together was a sure-fire success. In *It Happened Twice One Night* they were shown lying side by side on the terrace of a Manhattan penthouse shortly after they had been introduced to each other. They talked briefly of atomic energy and geep music and Mexican cookery. Then came this bit of dialogue:

Minervas and Maxes

WYATT: You have a lovely tail, my dear.
IMODELL: I think yours is nice, too.

The impact of those lines on the teen-age possessors of tails was more than enough to destroy forever the Minerva-Max movement. If Wyatt Vance called a tail a tail, then a tail was a tail. The terms Minerva and Max survived, as meaning artificial tails, and the ironical fact of the entire episode was this: Wyatt Vance and Imodell Parrish had no tails of their own. In that famous scene, she wore a Minerva and he wore a Max.

V

Some Dilemmas
and Perplexities

OF THE three hundred sixty-four million people in the United States today, a mere handful chooses to appear in public without tails. The production of artificial tails — Minervas and Maxes — for our older citizens has grown into an enormous business and this expansion was largely responsible for the garment industry's moving from New York City to Charlottesville.

Clothing is still manufactured without tail holes, but the No-Tail stores have become fewer and fewer and usually are found today stuck off in side streets. The scattering of men and women who refuse to attach artificial tails to their bodies includes certain rugged nonconformists who resist out of pure stubbornness and who seem to take pride in the fact that nothing depends from their behinds. There is also the Barebottom Club, a society of middle-aged men with small chapters in each of our major cities. Its

...this expansion was largely responsible for the garment industry's moving... to Charlottesville.

membership is devoted to a somewhat Rabelaisian view of the tail and the luncheon meetings of the Barebottoms are featured by ribald joking, service to the community, and the considerable consumption of an alcoholic drink called a Stingray. The members are almost all bachelors and are identifiable by a small silver button engraved with the word "NO" and worn on the seat of the trousers.

The millions of men and women over forty years of age who wear artificial tails have kept pace with the younger people who have natural tails, insofar as fads and fashions are concerned. In fact they have outdistanced the younger crowd, since there is a limit to what can be done with a real tail. Styles change, especially in Minervas, from year to year. The present fashion of eider-down tails for women was unthought of a year ago when natural skunk fur was the thing. The men who wear artificial tails have usually been satisfied with furled horsehide in solid browns and blacks (in the city) or various piebald effects (for country life) . It will be recalled that a few years ago, in both Los Angeles and New York, the better haberdashers featured tails of Shetland pony hide and these became quite popular among men of expensive tastes; the fad soon ended, however, when the limited supply of Shetland ponies

[47   ]

was exhausted. Efforts of our leading tail designers to invoke frequent style changes for men have met with stout consumer resistance, although there was a period about five years ago when executives of the big television networks (who previously had affected chamois tails) broke out with a rather radical departure. These men from the upper levels of TV administration began wearing tails loaded with porcupine quills. Their ancient adversaries, the advertising-agency men, responded with originality and imagination, affixing rattlesnake buttons to the tips of their tails. This rivalry was pursued in the good-natured spirit that is typical of American business relationships except when there is money involved.

The plastic base of the artificial tail, to which the fur or hide or eider down is cemented, has brought about the establishment of immense new chemical plants and the expansion of others; we scarcely need mention the incredible boom in the fur industry, where great fortunes have been made almost overnight. And God knows how many eider ducks have died in the last year in order that milady might have down for her tail. All of these elements enter into a vast production program which is unique in our industrial history — it is doomed to virtual extinction when the entire population has tails. The artificial tail will eventually disappear, or at least dwindle into a minor industry allied with surgical supplies, furnishing Minervas and Maxes for those unhappy individuals who have lost their tails through accident or disease. Concurrently, there will come a day when the complete history of artificial tails can be written and it will surely include some description of the "waggers" which were developed during the early 1990s.

Attempts to simulate real tails were given up about five years ago and today an artificial tail can be recognized for what it is by the simple manner of its general construction. The fact is, it could be recognized before, for the reason that it was a lifeless thing. No matter how genuine it looked, a woman could not communicate movement to her tail without wagging her posterior. This biodynamic fact produced an interesting social problem along about 1992. It was impossible for a woman who had reached the approximate age of thirty-five to conceal her years. One needed only to glance at her tail, noting the fact that it hung as if a plumb bob were attached to it, to know that she was at least in her middle thirties.

Many of these women deeply resented their inability to conceal their age. The tail, whether real or artificial, had already become one of woman's most enjoyable conceits. She devoted more time and energy to its grooming and enhancement than to any other of her daily pursuits. It was Gartersnake Smith, the rustic philosopher of Big Bend who appeared on the do-it-yourself television program *Thinking for the Beginner* and said:

"Used to be when you was talkin' about a woman's crowning glory, you was talkin' about 'er hair. Nowdays, you wanna git a look at 'er crowning glory, you gotta stand 'er on 'er head."

This female pridefulness must be taken into consideration when we talk about those women who, though still young and attractive, were compelled to wear tails that were dead. Their tails were fastened to the elastic harness that girdled their hips and could not be raised or lowered or wagged. Women, we must confess, are clever. Some of them managed to switch their tails by almost imperceptible hip jerks. On the other hand, many women who tried to impart movement to their tails were unable to conceal the hip jerks and consequently made their position all the more embarrassing.

Recognizing the dilemma of these aging women, several designers and engineers made an effort to produce artificial wagging devices. The most ridiculous of these (although it had a mild success for a time) was a battery-operated mechanism, consisting of two units which fitted into the armpits. A tiny control dial was kept concealed in the left hand. By manipulating this control, the matron could cause her tail to tremble or to elevate or to swing gently from side to side while she was standing perfectly still. The mechanism was faulty, however, and sometimes would slip a cog, producing a dull whirring sound such as might be made by an alarm clock held under water. So this particular "wagger" failed, as did less ambitious devices, and the women for whom they were intended had to resign themselves to tails of obvious artificiality.

Whereas the production of artificial tails will come to an end, there are many other industries which have been affected in a major way by tails and which will inevitably prosper as the years advance. The furniture industry, as we know, has been revolutionized. Every piece of furniture intended for sitting has had to be redesigned and the over-all effect has been the almost universal acceptance of the angular modernistic. Stools and chairs without backs are found today in most homes, and all chairs and sofas and love seats which do have backs are constructed for tail comfort. It is simply unthinkable for a person to sit on his tail for more than a few moments; provision must be made for the tail to stick through the furniture and extend out behind. This has been done as well in automobile seats, Pullman chairs and sections, airplane seats, church pews, and in all theaters and auditoriums. The folding seat in theaters, funeral parlors, baseball parks, and elsewhere has vanished. In the last year that the folding seat was used in Yankee Stadium, the management found itself facing law suits aggregating $7,450,000, filed by patrons who claimed that their tails had been permanently injured in the seats and that their personalities had been warped by the mental anguish and physical pain involved.

At this point let us note a minor but interesting development that has grown out of the redesign of furniture. The cat is disappearing as a household pet. Nothing fascinates a cat quite so much as a tail, even though it be his own. Zoologists have long known that a lioness teaches her cubs to be quick and accurate in pouncing by twitching her own tail and letting the cubs leap at it. A cat cannot leave a tail alone. Many of us have been unhappy witnesses on those occasions when a perfectly splendid dinner party has been disrupted by Pussy. Here sit the guests, ladies and gentlemen all, ranged around the table with their tails trailing out behind them. Quietly and unnoticed, the cat comes into the room. The moment he spies a tail, he is attracted to it as powerfully as if it were a barrel of catnip. He springs upon it, digging in his claws, and it is one of the great mysteries of animal behavior why he almost invariably chooses the tail of the most elegant and proper lady in the room. The author has seen one such lady, whose tail had just been attacked by a cat, leap screeching into the middle of the table, producing a wild scene of flying gravy and vegetables and crockery.

Today even people with artificial tails have gotten rid of their cats for the comfort and protection of tailed guests who come into their homes. There remain the aelurophiles, who would prefer death to giving up their cats. Yet even they have had to compromise. Several corporations now manufacture a sheath known as a "kittyguard" which is worn by those people who insist upon keeping cats; it is customary for these people to furnish extra kittyguards for their guests to wear. They are made of a strong plastic material and impregnated with a chemical which is offensive to cats.

The effect of the tail on domestic life has been of much more importance than the mere decline of the household cat. We shall attempt in subsequent chapters to deal with some of the changes that have been brought about in everyday life. For the time being, let us consider the tail as an irritant in the home. This matter has been studied at some length by Dr. Vladimir Slupnick, the eminent New York psychiatrist. Dr. Slupnick insists that the tail has been responsible for discord in many marriages. He has been quoted in the New York *World-Telegram & Sun & Herald-Tribune & Women's Wear Daily* as follows:

Minor irritations often lead to major breakups. We have always known that. Now the human tail has become a great source of irritation in the home. In the past many marriages collapsed because of lesser irritants. The habit, for example, of the husband who wiggles his foot while he reads his newspaper can become an infuriating thing to his wife and can lead, eventually, to her hating him. The tail looms today as an even greater cause of friction. Please remember the case of Cortland *versus* Cortland, and keep in mind the fact that similar disputes are occurring every day within the walls of the American home.

Dr. Slupnick had reference to the divorce proceedings involving Mr. and Mrs. Fenimore Cortland. Mr. Cortland was a well-to-do owner of a bucket shop in Wall Street, manufacturing buckets for dredging contractors. His wife, the former Virginia Flawless, attained a modicum of fame as Miss Chock Full o' Nuts of 1981. They had been married for four years and during that time had quarreled almost constantly. According to their own testimony, their quarreling always revolved around their tails.

Mrs. Cortland contended that her husband had a habit of twitching his tail from side to side in short jerks, both at home and in public, and that this twitching was a source of great irritation to her, and finally drove her to taking small doses of cocaine. Mr. Cortland, for his part, introduced medical evidence tending to show that his tail twitching was involuntary, that he suffered from a tic in the tail. It also appeared from the evidence that Mr. Cortland regarded his wife's tail as too inactive.

At one point in the trial the Cortland butler, Reeves, described their final quarrel, which occurred one evening after dinner while the Cortlands were watching a television program. According to the butler, who said he was eavesdropping in the hallway, the conversation went as follows:

MRS. CORTLAND: I wish you'd quit jerking that damn tail.

MR. CORTLAND: Please, Ginny, watch the show.

MRS. CORTLAND: How can I watch the show when your

The Age of the Tail

tail is jerking away like some damn donkey engine?

MR. CORTLAND: You don't have to sit and watch my tail. Watch the screen.

MRS. CORTLAND: I'm *not* sitting and watching your tail. How could any human being remain unaware of it, the way you keep it lolloping back and forth?

MR. CORTLAND: Now you listen to me, Miss Chock Full o' Meanness. Just keep your big mouth shut about my tail. This isn't your tail, it's my tail, and I'll do whatever I want to do with it. I'll jerk it clear off if I feel like it.

MRS. CORTLAND: Please, God, let him do it. Let him jerk it clear off before I do the job for him!

MR. CORTLAND: I resent that. As I've told you a thousand times before, it wouldn't hurt *you* to get a little life into your tail. Of all the dreary, dead, frigid pieces of meat and bone I've ever seen in all my life! You might as well have a broomstick stuck on your behind!

MRS. CORTLAND: You, you insolent, tail-jerking slob, I'll . . .

At this point, according to the butler's testimony, Mrs. Cortland lost all control of herself, sprang from her chair, grabbed her husband's tail with both hands, and began wrenching it around in a powerful grinding motion, as if she intended ripping it out by the roots. At the same time she kept up a continual screaming of, "Reeves, fetch a hatchet! Reeves, fetch a hatchet!" Mr. Cortland, in turn, managed to pivot himself around and get hold of his wife's tail, and while she shrieked for the butler, he began yelling, "I'll put some life in it! I'll give it some life!"

The butler's testimony continued:

Q. Why was your mistress calling for a hatchet?
A. I assume, sir, that it was her wish to hatch off the master's tail.
Q. Did you fetch her a hatchet?
A. No, sir.
Q. Why not?
A. The Cortlands kept no hatchet, sir.
Q. Are you a snoop, Reeves?
A. Oh, no, sir.

The divorce was granted on grounds of adultery.

V I

The New Neurotics

WE HAVE considered the problems of those women who were born in the years just before tails came in — women who today are in their forties and, because of the inertia of their tails, have difficulty passing themselves off as being in their thirties.

A more important matter, perhaps, concerns those people who were the first to have tails — those born in the beginning two or three years of the tail era. For the reason that their adolescent years were spent in confusion and uncertainty, and that many of them suffered a deep sense of shame in their childhood, they are inclined to be highly neurotic and antisocial today. They are often people with deep-seated animosities, which they are rarely able to conceal, and many of them are inclined to have an unconscious hatred of tails and of all things associated with tails. They will not, for example, ride in jet planes, or eat oxtail soup, or use commas.

...an unconscious hatred of tails...

The New Neurotics

Their unhappy heritage was exemplified in the famous Smirdoff-Clutcher affair which reached the courts of Los Angeles County fifteen years ago — a case which fully illustrates their mental instability. The story began, innocently enough, when Miss Hermione Smirdoff, a water-cress rancher living in the San Fernando Valley, announced that she was the first person in the world ever to have a tail. Miss Smirdoff, appearing on the television program *People Are Mixed Up*, dropped the remark that she was born in Ottumwa, Iowa, at precisely 5:35 A.M. on September 22, 1957. Subsequent to the television appearance she was widely photographed and interviewed, with special attention being given her tail. One Los Angeles newspaper had a close-up photograph taken of her tail and reproduced it on the front page, stretched across eight columns beneath the caption:

THE WORLD'S FIRST TAIL?

Miss Smirdoff was enjoying her burst of fame, had hired an agent, and was beginning to reap a tidy harvest in the endorsement of tail products, when Mrs. Carmen V. Clutcher of Roanoke, Virginia, appeared on the scene. Mrs. Clutcher bore an affidavit signed by a Roanoke physician saying he had delivered her a few seconds before 5:35 A.M. on the day tails came in.

Mrs. Clutcher was an attractive redhead with a magnificent matching tail. She installed herself in a Beverly Hills hotel and called in the reporters. She had a fine sense of the dramatic. When the reporters were all assembled, she stood up, turned sidewise, gestured gracefully toward her posterior, and said, "There, gentlemen, is the world's first tail." Then she flipped it upward, very much in the manner of a startled antelope. She made a highly favorable impression on the journalists and at least two of the reporters who were present fell in love with her on the spot.

Within a matter of hours these two young women were fighting furiously, using the press as their battleground, and day by day the quarrel grew more bitter and unreasonable. Mrs. Clutcher became so enraged at one point that she switched her attack to the physical condition of Miss Smirdoff's tail. It was true that Miss Smirdoff, by virtue of her rough employment as a water-cress rancher, had sustained an assortment of tail injuries; her tail was not quite straight and she could not maneuver it with facility. Certainly it could not compare with the splendid red-haired tail of Mrs. Clutcher.

The New Neurotics

A nation that had become extraordinarily tail conscious followed the dispute with avid eye and ear. The public generally had now aligned itself on the side of Miss Smirdoff. Most people were angered by Mrs. Clutcher's attack on the physical inadequacies of her antagonist's tail; such an attack was thoroughly unsportsmanlike and therefore, in the mind of the public, Miss Smirdoff was possessor of the world's first tail. It is difficult to fool the American public.

When Miss Smirdoff faced the television cameras to answer the attack, she spoke to a huge coast-to-coast audience. She spoke modestly, and her every word seemed to have the brand of sincerity on it. She told of her humble birth and childhood in Iowa, of how she had always known that her tail was the very first, and of how she had kept quiet about it because she was not "the bragging type." She told of her struggles to establish her water-cress ranch in the valley in order that she might make some worthwhile contribution to the nation — if only to the nation's tossed salads.

"Ladies and gentlemen," she said softly, "I now want you to meet my very dearest friend."

Into the studio came a short, stubby Nubian, stripped to the waist and wearing a turban. He was leading a water spaniel. When he unhooked the leash, the dog leaped into Miss Smirdoff's welcoming arms, and she turned back to her audience.

"This," she said, "is Cribbage. He is my friend and protector. He helps me in unbelievable ways in my duties around the ranch. And now I would like to call your attention to his tail."

She elevated the dog's hind quarters and the camera moved in on its tail. It was not a pleasant sight. Cribbage's tail was ragged and bent, with only small tufts of hair growing on it in three or four places.

Miss Smirdoff continued. "My darling's tail," she said, "got into this condition because he pursued his duty, because he wanted to make *his* contribution. He was staying close beside me, as he always does, guarding me against the multitude of evils that infest the world today, and he got his tail caught in my power mower."

She paused for a long moment.

"I suppose," she said, "that this horrible hag from Virginia will now make slighting remarks about the appearance of little Cribbage's tail. Well, let her. I have news for you tonight, my good people. I have here certain documents which tend to prove that this woman *actually has no tail!* She never, in all her life, had a true tail. The thing she is wearing is a graft job. Let her put *that* in her pipe and smoke it! Thank you, and good night."

It was said that there were few dry eyes among the millions who watched that telecast. But Mrs. Clutcher was not intimidated. Two days later she brought charges against Miss Smirdoff, accusing her of defamation, slander, false witness, and criminal libel.

Eventually the case came before Judge Suetonius Miller in Los Angeles. Both women were semi-hysterical throughout the court hearing, brandishing their tails defiantly, threatening to claw each other. Finally, during a period of comparative quiet, Mrs. Clutcher suddenly leaped from her chair and ripped off her skirt, revealing that she was wearing no underthings.

"Come on down here, Judge!" she yelled. "Come on down here and look at this tail! Come on down here and jerk on this tail!"

When order was finally restored, Judge Miller commanded the two disputants to stand before him.

"I'm going to throw this whole case out of court," he said. "I want you two ladies to go home and forget about which tail came first. A plague on both your tails!"

The Age of the Tail

They went home, but they didn't forget. In California Miss Smirdoff resumed her claim to primacy and found many advertisers who were willing to capitalize on her celebrity and on the fame of her dog. Back in Roanoke Mrs. Clutcher was divorced by her husband on grounds of incompatibility. She moved into a cottage on the outskirts of the city and put up a sign which said: "SEE THE WORLD'S FIRST TAIL. ADMISSION 25 CENTS." There was a flurry of interest for a while and she had as many as forty visitors a day, most of whom wanted to feel her tail. At the end of a year, however, people had lost interest in her and before long she dropped out of sight.

These two ladies, brought together by conflict, were individual examples of the psychological disturbance which so often affected those among us who were the first to be born with tails. It is in this group that we find today most of the so-called Single Cheek Reactionaries. They have refused to accept many of the changes that the tail has wrought in our mode of living. Their homes are equipped with old-style furniture, most of it overstuffed and solidly built with no opening for the tail. Rather than give in to the new age of functional design, they have retained divans and easy chairs just as they were in the past. And whenever they sit down, anywhere, they tilt themselves to one side or the other, resting their weight on one cheek for a while, then shifting to the other.

Surprisingly enough the Single Cheek Reactionaries have, except for a few dissenters, accepted one of the most radical alterations in household comforts. We shall discuss this change with some misgivings, though it must be given consideration if we are to have a complete picture of the tail's effect on our habits and customs.

When children with tails began to emerge from infancy, it became clear that one particular item in the home cried out for redesigning — the bathroom fixture associated with a sitting posture. As it stood, for obvious reasons, it would not do.

Engineers in the great plumbing-fixture establishments applied themselves to this problem, and it is amusing today to reflect on the amount of perspiring they did over a problem whose solution was so simple.

That solution: turn around and face the wall.

The new posture, simple as it was, nonetheless brought on interesting changes in the design of the fixture. As we know it today the top surface of the flush box has been lowered and enlarged to the size of a small table top, so that the occupant may rest his elbows on it if he is so inclined. This table top has become known generally as a "Terwilliger," after the man who designed it and worked out plans for its equipment. Most Terwilligers now are spread with colorful scarves or miniature tablecloths, and a small desk lamp is considered essential for those who want to look at picture books or catch up on their correspondence. This particular spot in the home has, in fact, become a place for working crossword puzzles, jigsaw puzzles, or for playing any of the multitude of new one-handed games that have been devised for bathroom use. In some of the better homes small television screens have been set into the wall behind the Terwilliger. In addition, one company has prospered in the manufacture of a special "Terwilliger kit" which is used by ladies to do their nails.

Save for the continued resistance of a few Single Cheek Reactionaries, the about-face in the bathroom is widely considered to have been a good thing. It is worth mentioning that Willis Padgett, whose narrative poem *Plush Wings at Ease* was awarded the Nick Kenny Memorial Prize, freely admitted in his acceptance speech that "I wrote every line of it on my Terwilliger."

In fact, one of the leading manufacturers of plumbing appliances, John K. Porsey, has publicly stated: "We in the industry ought to be ashamed of ourselves. We should have thought of this even before tails."

VII

Techniques in Tail Safety

DURING the last two decades the American Safety Council has taken an increasing interest in tail injuries and even at the present time is conducting a vigorous campaign of prevention.

Inasmuch as the tail is simply an extension of the spinal column, its physical construction in most people is both delicate and fragile. Abrasions or lacerations of the tail are considerably more serious than if they occurred on, say, the arm. A simple bruise can sometimes have serious consequences. It follows that a fall in which the victim alights in a seated posture has become a much more dangerous matter than it was previously. The scholarly journal *American Speech* has even noted that a blustering, threatening phrase once quite common in our language, namely, "I am going to knock you on your —— !" has all but disappeared because of the grave consequences inherent in the actual performance. It is considered to be as reprehensible as the act of strik-

[70]

ing a man in the face while he is wearing glasses.

In its recent surveys the Safety Council has determined that the greatest number of accidents involving the tail occur in the home. Of these home accidents, a majority occur in the bathtub. Slipping and falling in the bathtub was a major hazard even in the days before tails, but now it has become much more dangerous. Four out of five persons who slip in the bathtub, according to the Safety Council, injure their tails. The council has urged that the American people cease taking showers, and that the manufacturers redesign the tub itself, providing a depressed section in the rear for the greater convenience and comfort of the bather with a tail.

Thus far the manufacturers have resisted this pressure, arguing that sitting on a shelf in a tub would entail, or, rather, involve, more discomfort than sitting on a flat surface. They point out that the normal person, when seated properly, has a space of an inch and a half to two inches between the surface on which he is sitting and the point at which his tail emerges from the sacrum. Granted, says the Safety Council, but many people like to relax in their bath — to lie back in the tub in a semireclining position, and this is impossible without the depressed area. The argument is typical of many another dispute that has arisen as a result of man's new organism.

The Safety Council has long been disturbed by the increase in tail injuries in industry. In its pamphlet *The Basic Problem in Tail Safety* (1986) the council recognized several fundamental factors. This report says:

Workers in industry are subject to the same emotional responses as people elsewhere. A factory worker has moments of great anger and indignation as well as moments of euphoria during the course of his day. In such circumstances, his tail is likely to fly up suddenly, or begin wagging from side to side. Therein lies the danger. If the worker's tail remained pendant throughout the day, there would be far fewer accidents. A great majority of the serious accidents in our factories occur when a worker's tail, responding to anger over a fancied injustice or leaping upward at the passage of an attractive girl through the plant, gets caught in the machinery. We already know that it is both foolish and hopeless to attempt solving the problem by trapping the tail inside the clothing, or strapping it to the leg. Tests have been conducted in which groups of workers have voluntarily had their tails trussed for extensive periods of time. These tests show that the efficiency of the worker is reduced appreciably if his tail is not given free play. On the other hand, the efficiency of the tail apron has been demonstrated in many trades. The tail apron must always be constructed to fit the type of job being performed by its wearer. Thus he will be protected against most ordinary cuts and bruises. His apron will not save him, however, if he happens to get his tail caught in

The council urges that ... manufacturers redesign the tubs ...

machinery. It remains for the employer to install safeguards — metal shields of various kinds covering each part of a machine where there is a possibility that a tail might be dragged in.

The Safety Council's remarks on tail aprons need a little elaboration here. The reader will recall our mention, in Chapter V, of the "kittyguard," the sheath employed to prevent injury from pouncing cats. The kittyguard is a form of the tail apron. There are today dozens of types of tail aprons, including even the common "duster" worn by most housewives — a simple cotton affair which women slip on while doing the housework to keep dust and grime from getting into their tails. There are more rugged tail aprons, made of canvas or leather or plastics, that are by now associated with various pursuits. The automobile mechanic, for example, wears a cheap but sturdy canvas tail apron which keeps grease and oil from getting to his tail but which permits him to crawl about under cars (the dolly on which he sometimes rides has been redesigned and equipped with a tail trough). Carpenters, painters, and plumbers also wear canvas tail aprons and in recent years these coverings have come to serve as a sort of badge, identifying one trade from another. Most people today know that a man wearing a blue tail apron is a carpenter, that a plumber wears red, a paper hanger wears blue polka dots on white, a stone mason wears purple, a hod carrier wears pink, a painter wears an apron of a mottled or speckled appearance, a tree surgeon wears dark green, a gardener wears light green, railroad workers affect red and green stripes, a television repairman wears alternating wavy blue and white stripes, and so on. This trade identification often extends into the home, where, for example, the wife of a paper hanger will usually wear a polka dot tail apron similar to her husband's, though of lighter material.

The tail aprons used in industrial plants, however, are usually of an exceeding toughness. The plastics industry has come up with some fine resilient materials which serve to protect the factory worker's tail as completely as if it were encased in armor. A fairly recent improvement on industrial tail aprons is the trip hook, designed for workers who are on their feet most of the time. At the tip end of the tail apron is a small hook which the worker fastens to a patented clasp on his trouser leg. Thus the tail is kept in the same place, out of the way, and given sufficient movement to prevent stiffness. If for some reason it leaps upward in the course of the day, a slight pull on the patented clasp releases the hook and the worker is not subjected to the painful frustration which would otherwise result.

A word about farmers must be included. The American farmer has always been an ingenious man and in many rural areas he has taken it upon himself to devise methods for the protection of his tail. Some of his contrivances are crude, but effective. The homemade tail pan is perhaps the most common — a pan or trough of either metal or wood which is bolted to the seat of the cultivator, rotary plow, corn picker, hay tedder, or tractor. The farmer simply stretches his tail out in this pan and goes about his business with utter peace of mind. In some sections of the South tail suspenders are favored by farmers. These are simply elastic supporters which elevate the tail out of danger. They are inspired, no doubt, by the crupper and they are usually homemade, although several companies are now manufacturing, on a small scale, tail suspenders for the farm.

The problem of tail injuries is still a headache for the insurance companies. For years they resisted suggestions that they write policies covering injuries to or loss of tails. The attitude of the insurance companies was summarized more than twenty years ago by Clayton E. Foster, chairman of the board of the

The Age of the Tail

Greeley Indemnity Corporation. In a speech at Philadelphia Mr. Foster said:

> We don't insure hair. We wouldn't insure a man against baldness. The same principle is involved here. We will insure a person against loss of hands or feet or arms or legs or fingers or eyes. Such losses constitute disability, or partial disability. The tail is another matter altogether. It is ornamental rather than utilitarian. A lawyer, a waiter, a brakeman, a ditch digger, even an insurance salesman can go about his work whether he has a tail or no. If we did ever descend to the ridiculous and start insuring tails against injury, the premiums would be prohibitive. Few citizens would be able to afford such coverage.

The United States being an insurance-minded nation, there was continuing pressure on the big companies to provide such policies. Actuaries were put to work, but they achieved very little beyond trying to place a valuation on the tail by inches — so much to be paid per inch of tail lost. The high percentage of tail injuries, as compared with injuries to hands and feet and arms and legs, left them in a state of doubt and confusion.

Since all insurance companies are subject to regulation by state agencies, the matter reached a climax through the intervention of one such governmental bureau. The Insurance Commissioner for the State of Kansas announced that all companies

[78]

operating in his domain would be compelled to insure tails. The companies struck back, issuing a statement in which they charged that the Insurance Commissioner was prejudiced. They said that the commissioner's oldest son had got his tail caught in the rear wheel of his motorcycle and lost nineteen inches of it, and that the commissioner had three other sons who were beginning to ride motorcycles and might conceivably lose portions of their tails. The insurance companies accused the commissioner of cupidity, stating flatly that he was only interested in collecting compensation on tail losses in his own family. The commissioner denied this accusation with great vehemence, proclaiming himself to be a man of unsullied integrity, dedicated to the welfare of the people.

The stir created by this dispute actually hastened the process by which some of the larger companies began writing tail policies. As of today they still refuse to insure a tail against minor hurts or tail diseases; they will pay only in case of amputation, or partial amputation. And they refuse to use the word "disability" in any of these policies, holding to Mr. Foster's dictum that the loss of a tail or part of a tail is the same as a man's going bald.

V I I I

The Medical Story

IT IS a tribute to the American version of the human
spirit that our people have taken to the tail with
such gusto, devoting great time and energy to its
decoration and protection and devising a complex
code of manners to govern its movement. This is
particularly true since, in all candor, we must confess that the new member has considerable nuisance
value.

The English skeptic Virgil Smith-Willoughby has
written:

> That was an accursed day when the tail came to the
> human race. Ordinary day-to-day living had already be-
> come a tribulation, and now was added a ridiculous ap-
> pendage which served in turn as a dust catcher, a bug
> colony, a disease carrier — a senseless scourge far more
> troublesome than the vermiform appendix. Clearly, we
> would be far better off if horns had sprouted from our
> heads rather than tails from our posteriors.

Though we hesitate to agree with anything said
or written by this negative thinker, we must concur

in the suggestion that the pathology of the human tail is an unhappy story. Assiduous care must be given to it if we hope to escape from the pernicious ailments and pests which assault the tail from every quarter.

Yet the story is not without its bright side. Let Smith-Willoughby reflect on the fact that the cure for cancer was discovered by Dr. Thaddeus Warble while he was seeking a specific for the treatment of tail measles in children. The miracle drug which Dr. Warble obtained from the green mold scraped off the backs of wrist watches and strap buckles in the summertime (the drug called "Embraceable" from the name of the watch on which it was first discovered) turned out to be effective in the cure of carcinoma.

Both the medical profession and the chemical industry have seen great changes brought about by the variety of ailments and afflictions which plague the tail. The chief weapon against them continues to be tail hygiene, which requires unremitting attention. Any person possessing normal self-respect should cleanse his tail at least once a day; it is a known fact, however, that the great majority of our citizens are inclined to neglect this duty, even in the face of repeated warnings that if such general neglect continues, the consequences could be disastrous to the race. Yet the campaign to educate the people in tail hygiene goes on apace and ground is being gained.

The seriousness with which the nation is taking tail hygiene may be demonstrated by citing two recent developments:

1. The 1991 fiat from the Bureau of Manners and Morals in Washington which declares that it is as improper for one person to wear another's tail apron as it is to use his toothbrush, and making such an act a misdemeanor punishable by fine.

2. The statement of a Defiance College physiologist that the human race is becoming slope-shouldered and is developing elbows with swivel-action joints as a result of the time spent in reaching for and working on the tail.

While the medical profession and health authorities recommend a daily tail wash as the best means of combating infection, most people have fallen into the habit of cleansing their tails three times weekly. The nation's arbiters of etiquette in Washington (BMM) have sought to impress the public with the importance of frequent tail shampoos by emphasizing the social ostracism that may come as a consequence of tail odor. They have used familiar

Cleanse the tail once daily.

The Medical Story

techniques developed long ago by the advertising
profession in reference to body odor and fetid
breath. The untreated tail itself exudes a mildly un-
pleasant odor which seems to combine, in attenu-
ated form, the smells associated with the musk ox
and the Toggenburg goat. Virtually all well-bred
men today use sticky or oily dressings and pomades
on their tails, and these applications pick up and
retain certain odors, such as tobacco smoke, carbon
monoxide, stale vegetation, and kitchen effluvia.
These acquired smells combine with natural tail
odor to produce an effect on squeamish people that
sometimes leads to hospitalization.

The multitudes who, out of laziness or indifference, refuse to follow the prescribed rules of tail
hygiene often advance the argument that "proper
people don't go around bending over and smelling
the tails of other people." They forget that there are
many conditions under which one person may find
himself with the tail of another person in his face;
e.g., in all places where some people are standing
and some sitting, such as crowded subway cars or
buses, the theater and motion-picture houses, cock-
tail parties, railway stations and airline terminals.

In discussing the medical aspects of the tail, we
must not neglect mention of a most important

[85]

physiological fact — the close connection between
the tail and the brain. The area of the brain which
sends out impulses calling for the movement of the
tail is situated in front of the fissure of Rolando, an
extremely sensitive and susceptible spot. The tail,
being an extension of the spinal column, is in closer
communication with the brain than any of the other
extremities; messages from the tail go right straight
up the line to the control tower. By the same principle, certain infections and injuries to the tail have
a direct path, with no turnings and no stop lights,
to the brain. This way lies insanity.

We shall make no attempt in these pages to
enumerate all the injuries and diseases that afflict
the tail. We have already mentioned wry tail, sometimes called *tail torticollis*, which is the same thing
as having a stiff neck in the tail. The expression
"Charley horse of the tail" is often heard nowadays,
as describing a strained muscle, but the usage is
incorrect because "Charley horse" properly belongs
to the thigh. If employed at all, the correct usage
would be "Charley tail."

Myositis of the tail has become a fairly common
complaint and develops after the tail has been ex-
posed to wet or cold, or when the victim has been
sitting with his tail in a draft.

The Medical Story

Such afflictions as slipped disc, calcium deposits, and an injury similar to chipped elbow are known to doctors, and adequate methods of treatment have been devised for them. Most of the skin diseases found on other parts of the body are often present in the tail — it is highly susceptible to sebaceous cyst, impetigo, and erysipelas. Of these, contagious impetigo is the most common and has become known as "commuter's tail." The popular name for bursitis of the tail is "stenographer's tail." *

The reader may recall our mention of the Cortland divorce case earlier in this survey and the contention of Mr. Cortland that he suffered from a tic in his tail. Such things are by no means uncommon. A tic can be either a habit spasm or a mimic spasm. It manifests itself in the tail through a periodic twitching or jerking. Most physicians are now agreed that tail tics are largely psychosomatic and that psychotherapy is essential in treating them, although muscular drill and breathing exercises have been found to be beneficial, serving to re-establish natural body rhythms.

Thus far our surgeons have not been altogether

* In the past the various forms of bursitis gave rise to such locutions as miner's elbow, housemaid's knee, tennis elbow, and tailor's bottom.

successful in tail grafting. Experimental work continues, however, notably at James Millikin University and USCSF (University of Southern California at San Francisco) in an atmosphere of optimism. Dr. Pierpont Towle of James Millikin recently told the Decatur *Review:*

> Within five years tail grafting will have become as common as nose bobbing. Certainly there is a great need for it. Before long many citizens will be making provisions in their wills, bequeathing their tails to others. Tail banks will be established in all our major cities. I must say that one of the serious problems facing us in the future is that of keeping the human tail alive after it is severed. I have tried it in plain salt water, but that doesn't work. The tail simply twitches a few times and then gives up the ghost. You may rest assured, however, that we'll find the answer.

In any discussion of the medical and surgical aspects of the tail, mention must be made of the increasing conflict between physicians and surgeons on the one hand and chiropractors and osteopaths on the other. This ancient quarrel has grown much more violent since the coming of the tail, possibly because of the unprecedented increase in the number of chiropractors and osteopaths now practicing. Great numbers of people who never went to them before now take their musculoskeletal tail difficul-

The Medical Story

ties to either the chiropractor or the osteopath. Medical men have lately begun speaking scornfully of "tail crackers" and "butt rubbers," yet the objects of their contempt continue to prosper.

There is something to be said on both sides of the dispute. Certain it is that quacks and mountebanks have appeared in the dignified ranks of the regular medical profession. We only need refer to the case of Dr. Hobe Wincing, who appeared before the convention of the American Medical Association in 1982 and read a paper in which he claimed that whooping cough could be contracted through the tail. An investigative committee found Dr. Wincing guilty of unethical conduct in seeking personal publicity, and he was expelled from the association. It may be noted, too, that the medical profession is not always of a single mind in matters pertaining to the tail. Ten years ago there was a violent dispute within the profession, one group contending that little children should be allowed to cling to their mothers' tails, another faction insisting that any child that hung onto its mother's tail would surely grow up to be either a sex maniac or a hermit.

We come now to the most common of all tail ailments and, potentially, the most dangerous — tail

[89]

itch. It is improbable that any possessor of a tail has completely escaped it.

Certain forms of tail itch come from skin infections, but the villain in the vast majority of cases is a bug — either the flea, the mite, or the louse. Health authorities have been both astonished and dismayed by the increase and spread of these tiny creatures amongst all segments of our population. They are continually warning us that unless the situation is brought under control, we face a recurrence of the bubonic plague as well as epidemics of typhus, American relapsing fever, elephantiasis, and Chagas' disease. The unremitting campaign to educate the people in tail hygiene is, in large measure, a campaign for the control of these bugs.

Common tail itch, or tail scabies, is caused by the mite *Acarus scabiei*. Another troublesome mite, the chigger, has spread to every part of the continent. And at least two members of the arachnid family, which formerly confined themselves to specific feeding grounds, have now transferred their operations to the human tail. One of these is the cheese mite, and the other is the clover mite. The latter formerly lived almost exclusively in deciduous orchard trees, such as the apple, pear, cherry, plum, and peach. During the last generation all the clover mites have left their orchard trees and taken up residence on the human tail, creating enormous discomfort for people everywhere. The changeover has, however, been a great boon to fruit growers.

Fleas are simply everywhere. There are more than five hundred known species of flea. In the past the individual species have usually demonstrated "host specificity" — favoring a particular bird or mammal as their feeding grounds. For example, one particular type of flea was never found anywhere except on coyotes; the coyote flea has somehow taken a liking to the human tail, and transferred his attention to it. The same thing is true of at least two hundred other species.

The flea has always been the most proficient jumper known to nature. In the past he could leap about thirteen inches — an almost incredible performance considering his size. Experiments conducted at Sweet Briar College have shown that fleas can now jump at least fifteen and a half inches. This considerable increase in his leaping power is attributed to the new conditions under which the flea lives — leaping from tail to tail. A person who gives the most meticulous attention to his tail hygiene cannot escape the flea, short of locking himself in a fumigated closet. And yet the flea is not the tail's most formidable enemy. Let us be frank, and face up to the fact that the Number One pest is the louse.

The louse family, responsible for the maddening condition known as pediculosis, formerly had three divisions: the head louse, the body louse, and the crab louse. As a general rule each of these creatures stayed in his own bailiwick. Today there is a fourth member of the clan, the tail louse. He is the result of interbreeding between the body louse and the crab louse, and he has become by far the most numerous of all. A single female can produce over five thousand progeny in about eight weeks.

The louse is not the most dangerous of the pests attacking the tail, but surely he is the most bothersome; he is probably responsible for eighty-five per cent of all cases of tail itch. It would seem almost that the human tail was designed for his habitation — that is, the tail and its accoutrements. He lives usually in the tail collar, which provides him with comfortable shelter, and travels down the tail itself only when seeking food. Both his traveling and his feeding titillate the sensitive skin, producing an almost uncontrollable urge in the victim to scratch. Long ago an anonymous Frenchwoman, speaking of the pestiferousness of lice and fleas, said, "Quant

The Medical Story

à moi, ce n'est pas la morsure, c'est la promenade."
(It isn't so much the bite, it's the walking about.)
Fortunately, a method has been devised for restricting the louse to the tail. He has an unhappy tendency to stray far afield, seeking greener pastures, especially at night when his host is in bed. The medicated tail garter has been designed to halt the invader, so to speak, at the border. This small elastic garter snaps around the base of the tail and is impregnated with certain chemicals which are offensive to the louse. So long as the garter is worn, he will rarely venture into new territory.

As concerns these particular pests, we must mention two attitudes adopted by their victims generally. Socially the louse has always ranked far below the flea. That social stratification obtains today. The very word "louse" is seldom heard (except in reference to people) and almost no one admits he exists. People have come to talk freely, however, about the flea. It would be difficult today to find a person who admitted that his tail itch was the result of an infestation of lice. Instead he usually says, "Those damned fleas have got to me again in spite of all those treatments." This public refusal to accept and identify the tail louse has had an interesting industrial effect. As we know, the manufacturing establishments which were previously devoted to various flea powders and sprays for the control of pests in domestic animals have grown enormously. The city of Richmond, for example, has long since abandoned the tobacco business and is today almost a one-industry town, with its acres and acres of plants turning out powders and sprays and ointments for the human tail. The research chemists have developed many preparations aimed directly at the control of the tail louse, yet they are never marketed as such. They are specifically for the destruction of the louse, but they are always labeled "Flea Powder" or "Flea Spray." The manufacturers know that it would be almost impossible ever to sell a product frankly called "Louse Killer."

The other public attitude we have in mind fits more closely into the realm of etiquette. Public scratching of the tail is, of course, considered to be vulgar. The problem became so acute, however, that some acceptable method for obtaining relief had to be found. It came in the form of the tail brush. This small, curving, semicircular brush has stiff bristles and fits tightly over the ordinary tail. And while scratching with the fingers is held to be wholly improper, it has become perfectly acceptable for either a man or a woman to brush the tail in public, even though such brushing actually amounts to scratching. That is why almost everyone today carries a tail brush, and why people in every walk of life spend a great deal of time in public wielding that brush.

Concluding this brief summarization of the medical history of the tail, let us remark the revival of an old superstition. There are many people today who believe that they can forecast weather by the activity of the fleas on their tails. This belief goes back to an early English rhyme which went:

> When eager bites the thirsty flea
> Clouds and rain you sure shall see.

There may be some truth in it, although not likely.

I X

Let the Peacock Blush!

THE PUBLICATION of picture books has brought on
a literary renaissance in the United States during
the last ten years. For a long while the book business
languished, growing steadily weaker in the face of
public indifference to reading matter.* Now things
are looking up for those few publishers who managed to survive, and the market is being flooded
with volumes of photographs which contain very
little text.

The current rage is for books which illustrate the
American way of life as it was in the early 1950's,
immediately prior to the advent of tails. These photographs of a people without tails and without any
suspicion that they would soon acquire tails are ex-

* The production of history and biography has continued on
a reduced scale, but because of the lack of public support,
these projects have been either subsidized by the government
or financed by grants from the big foundations. The research
and the writing of the present volume could not have been
undertaken but for a Moral Rearmament fellowship.

tremely amusing to the new generation. Our children are thoroughly fascinated by them; it is difficult for them to visualize a world in which no human being had a tail. They seek out their grandparents and pepper them with questions. They say, "It must have felt funny!"

The one aspect of daily life which makes the most profound impression on the children is that of costume. Even our older citizens, those who had reached maturity before 1957, are bemused by the photographs. Some of them insist that things were better in the old days, that life was less complicated and far less troublesome. It must be kept in mind, however, that these dissenters are people who have no true tails, but only artificial ones. It is hard to convince them that there are compensating pleasures in the possession of a tail — the invigorating sensations, for example, that accompany brisk wagging, or an abrupt rising of the tail to the gay position during moments of excitement.

Children of today are almost as much impressed by the absence of tail collars in the early 1950s as they are by the absence of the tail itself. They look at a photograph showing the blank seat of a man's trousers and they react as if they were viewing a man's face without a nose. As suggested above, there is something a little horrifying to them in a human posterior without a tail — they seem to feel that not having a tail would be painful.

The evolution of the tail collar was a slow process, for it had to follow the development of the tail itself. There were no fancy collars until around 1980. Up to that time the tail hole in children's garments was little more than that — a tail hole. In the early 1970s the plain tail collar of cotton rickrack began to appear among teen-agers. Gradually this bordering grew more elaborate and today the tail collar has become one of the chief concerns of fashion designers.

As might be expected, the ladies have outdone the men in the way of splendor. A well-dressed man of today has, in his bedroom, a rack containing at least a dozen collars, usually more. It has become a part of his routine each morning to select the tail collar he plans to wear during the day and hook it into the seat of his pants, just as in former times he selected the day's necktie.* The male collar is usually of a simple circular design, and of solid color.

---

* For the benefit of younger readers, the necktie was a long strip of colored cloth which men wrapped around their necks, tied into a knot at the throat, and wore throughout the day in the belief that it made them more presentable and more attractive.

Let the Peacock Blush!

The star-shaped collar has, however, met with a certain amount of popularity and a few years back we had the bull's-eye collar, fashioned after the manner of a target.

Women, or at least the designers for women, have been much more imaginative. Every known kind of fur is employed nowadays for their collars, plus ornamental materials such as silver lamé and gold brocade. Where the female tail collar is of the ordinary circular kind, its beauty is often enhanced by sequins or more expensive gems. But women have not been content to stay with the circular design. The vast advertising campaigns built around the tail collar testify to that. It would be a rare person who has not seen one of the thousands of billboards scattered over the nation proclaiming:

SET OFF YOUR TAIL
WITH
SUNBURST!

The ladies, in fact, seem to be going more and more for eccentric design in their collars. The spider has become one of the most popular forms. The tail emerges from the center of the spider's body, and the creature's eight legs are outspread, covering almost all of the posterior and actually seeming to grasp it. Psychiatrists have devoted considerable

[99]

The Age of the Tail

speculation to this particular design and are even now in dispute about it. Some contend that it is a subconscious choosing of a symbol that is anathema to insect pests; others contend, because of the position of the spider's legs, that it is altogether sexual. It is pointed out by the latter group that the octopus design had a flurry of popularity after the spider collar had become established; in the case of the octopus tail collar, the creature's eight arms were given a realistic, writhing, grasping appearance, extending around the hips to the front of the costume and seeming to hold the entire hip area in a firm embrace. The octopus is not seen much any longer and then only in the larger cities.

Needlepoint and beaded work are being used extensively for ladies' collars. The reader may recall the publicity given the New York dramatic actress, Miss Barbara Seville, a few seasons back when she wore the same tail collar for three months — a splendid, squarish, beaded collar bearing the words: "I Love Joe Kitchly." Miss Seville's public declaration of her affections led to a nationwide fad for tail collars inscribed with a message, usually sentimental. The fashion even worked its way into politics. In last year's presidential campaign, supporters of Kenneth G. Harsie, the Bingo Party candidate, wore tail collars of imitation needlepoint inscribed with the injunction: "Harsie, Keep Your Tail Up!"

The inscribed tail collar is dwindling in its appeal, possibly for two reasons. Broadway and Hollywood characters have employed it for comic purposes. Some of the "gag collars" which we've either seen or read about bore such inscriptions as: "Down, Boy!" "I Wear No Man's Collar," "No Leapfrog Allowed," "Don't Tread on Me," "Tail of Two Cities," "Here's a Switch," and "The End." These japes were found to be amusing by the so-called sophisticates of café society and the Broadway columnists, but the practice has died down, probably for lack of writers.

The death knell of the inscribed tail sampler was, however, really composed in the spring of the present year after the advertising agencies moved in. Through the liberal application of money the admen persuaded a large number of celebrities, most of them society women, to permit the space on their tail collars to be used for display advertising. This new expression of the huckster's art was becoming a big business operation when the memorable case of Mrs. Cornelius Van Wyck Bordaline, of New York and Palm Beach society, brought it to an undignified end.

The Age of the Tail

Mrs. Bordaline, it will be recalled, was walking up Park Avenue at dusk one afternoon. Her tail collar bore the words "I USE MUM," spelled out across her ample bottom in tiny electric bulbs which flashed on and off as she moved northward. For a while a group of street urchins trailed along in her wake, shouting vulgar remarks, but eventually these tormentors grew tired of the game. Mrs. Bordaline appeared to be completely indifferent to their taunts (she was being paid two hundred and fifty dollars an hour for every hour she walked the streets with her lights blinking). She was approaching Fifty-fourth Street when a small man, later described as having had an extremely short tail, came up behind her. Using an instrument that resembled a broom-stick, he began beating her lustily across the advertisement. Mrs. Bordaline's screams attracted other pedestrians, but by the time they reached her side, the attacker had faded into the gloom. At the hospital, doctors spent three hours picking small bits of glass and wire from Mrs. Bordaline's body and treating her for severe tail bruises, and when, at last, she was able to talk, she told detectives: "I made a mistake. I should not have permitted the employment of my tail area for commercial purposes. However, I do hope you catch that little son of a bitch

Let the Peacock Blush!

and strangle him." He was never caught. Many people believe that the police made no more than a pretense of searching for him. In all events, very little advertising has been seen on tail collars since that day. In fact the only inscriptive decorations considered proper nowadays are tastefully designed monograms and fraternal insignia (such as a scimitar poised over a Shriner's tail). It may be that civilization owes a debt to Mrs. Bordaline.

The revolution in costume has been, to put it simply, a change in design to accommodate the tail. For example, the old-style jacket worn for generations by men has disappeared and the much more attractive bolero has become universal in Western civilization. It is all but impossible today to buy pajamas; they have been succeeded by the waist-length nightshirt, worn by both sexes. The long overcoat has gone the way of pajama pants. Women's girdles have snug-fitting elastic tail holes in them. The tail muff has come into being for those who are unduly sensitive to weather.

The real commercial revolution, however, is reflected in our department stores and in the smaller establishments catering exclusively to the tail needs of the public. The enormous Macy-Cimbel store in Manhattan has two entire floors devoted to tail accessories. The author has just completed a brief tour through these two floors and can report having seen, among many other items, the following:

A vast assortment of tail-hair dyes, tints, and rinses.
Cooling lotions, such as mentholated ointments.
Tail perfumes, domestic and imported.
Dandruff applications in both liquid and paste form.
Tail dressings. This is the popular term now used for those applications containing bornate, nicotine, pyrethrum, and so on, which are advertised so incessantly on television for the control of fleas, mites, and lice.
Lanolin preparations. Among these is an ointment prepared from the wool of karakul lambs, retailing at $32 the ounce.
Almond squeezings ("for softer, more romantic tails").
Vitamin C in aspic.
Packaged bone-meal pudding.
Undertail deodorants.
Dado mirrors.
Home tail dyer (with pellets). This is a long metal cylinder fastened to a tripod so that it can be tilted downward at an angle. The opening may be adjusted to the exact height of the tail base (or tail head). The cylinder is filled with two quarts of water which is heated electronically and into which the colored pellets are dropped. Subject inserts tip of tail into opening, then backs up until the entire tail is in. Subject then stands for fifteen minutes before removing tail. (This device, we were assured, is now perfectly safe to use. Early models of the home tail dyer were found to be deleterious. They not only dyed the hair, they also dyed the skin of the tail, causing a form of hives

'Tail Bendix. Based on the principle of the home laundry...

and burning sensations. The trouble lay in the composition of the pellets, which contained coal-tar derivatives. This has been corrected.)

Tail Bendix. Based on the principle of the home laundry — an electronic machine for quick and thorough tail washing through tumbling action.

Westinghouse Tail Fluffer. A hot-air chamber in which a wet tail can be quickly dried and fluffed. Used mainly after a bath.

Tail aprons. In addition to the hundreds of vocational types, kittyguards, and so on, these include brightly colored rubber sheaths which serve to protect the tail from the erosive effects of salt water at the beach.

Gold expansion bands. Usually worn three at a time, spaced about an inch apart near the middle of the tail.

Charm bracelets.

Rings. The wearing of signet rings on the tail has become quite popular. The practice originated at Northwestern University, where coeds began wearing large-sized fraternity rings on their tails, signifying their romantic preferences.

Tail beads. These range from strings of cheap glass to ropes of expensive pearls. Fashion dictates that beads should always be wound counterclockwise away from the base of the tail.

Barrettes.

Assorted tufts and tassels.

Flags and banners.

The last named articles deserve more than a mere listing, for they reflect the obstinacy of the female sex when it comes to fashion.

The Age of the Tail

For six or seven years now many women have been tying knots in their tails. Leading doctors have inveighed against the practice, but to no avail. As Professor Goldwyn Mersh has aptly said: "A woman will endure any discomfort and even jeopardize her health for the sake of fashion."

Not all women are able to tie knots in their tails. But those who can do it without suffering too much pain follow the practice on holidays and other special occasions. The knot is usually formed about a foot from the tip of the tail and must be drawn tight, and into the knot is fixed a small flag or pennant. An American flag on Independence Day, a green flag on Saint Patrick's Day, college pennants at graduation time — these are some of the uses to which the tail knot is put. Occasionally one sees a rose, a gardenia, or even an orchid decorating the knot.

It is interesting to note that almost every tail fad and fashion that comes along evokes a burlesque of itself. In the case of the knot, the burlesque seems to be exclusively in the hands of a lady who operates a delicatessen in the neighborhood of New York's Columbus Circle. Each day she appears for business with either a pickle, a weenie, or a small herring

Let the Peacock Blush!

stuck in the knot of her tail. "It brings in trade," she says.

Let us take notice, too, of one Bates Carhart, a ninety-four-year-old citizen of North Carolina who was interviewed recently by the Shelby *Daily Star.*

"I shore have to laugh," said Mr. Carhart, "at all these women a-goin' around with knots tied in their fool tails. Why, when I was a boy, back around the time of the First World's War, back in the *good* days I mean, our parents used to have a sayin'. Whenever one of us kids did somethin' ornery, they'd say to us, 'You behave yerself er I'll jerk a knot in yer tail!' Hodamighty! These modern females, they jerk their *own* knots!"

X

Tail Etiquette

W HEN the Bureau of Manners and Morals was established it was the hope of the government that its rulings in the realm of etiquette would be accepted by the people as quasi-judicial. It was felt that a simple rule of etiquette as set forth in the bureau's Blue Book would have much the same effect as an ordinance, similar to the unwritten law of former times which commanded that a man remove his hat when the flag passed. The official rules, however, had no such effect and were ignored generally, so that it became necessary for the bureau to institute a system of penalties for certain flagrant violations of the code.

It must be admitted that since the bureau was established there has been a distinct improvement in manners. Yet in many cases its rulings are still disdained. One of its first decrees concerned the proper time for arrival at dinner parties. The Blue Book states flatly that whenever a person is invited to dinner and told to arrive at seven o'clock, he should make every effort to arrive precisely at that time. A great public outcry followed the announcement of this ruling. People who have readily submitted to the bureau's severe directives in morals and censorship howled that their constitutional rights were being invaded, that they would happily suffer imprisonment before they'd ever arrive at a dinner party on time. The rule remains in the book, but it is ignored, and most people continue the time-honored custom of arriving from thirty minutes to an hour and a half late at such parties.

Since its formation the bureau has stopped the publication of all books dealing with questions of etiquette, and the day of the individual arbiter in this field has ended. The rules have been revised and codified and today a staff of four thousand men and women, including three thousand field workers, is keeping them up to date. As yet the etiquette of the tail has not been integrated into the general text, but is contained in an Appendix which this year covers forty-four pages.

Inasmuch as the Blue Book is available to all citizens at a token cost of $12, we shall make no attempt to detail its coverage of the tail. In the preparation of this brief survey we have often consulted

The Age of the Tail

the Blue Book and many of the proprieties mentioned elsewhere in these pages are approved in Washington.

It is nonetheless interesting to note the year-by-year expansion of the Appendix. New problems involving the tail are constantly being considered and dealt with by the bureau. For example, one of the new rules this year advises parents on the proper method for administering a spanking to their children: "Hold the child's tail up with the left hand, spank with the right; if parent is left-handed, reverse the procedure."

A quick glance through the Appendix is sufficient to convince anyone that not many tail problems have been overlooked. Let us examine just a few, picked at random:

B: 24 — Never apply insect powder or sprays in public unless specifically instructed to do so by your doctor.

L: 16 — In the theater, hold the tail with one hand while moving in and out of seat rows, to prevent brushing others in the face.

L: 28 — Never summon a waiter or other servitor by yanking on his tail.

G: 90 — Whereas in the past it was considered rude and unmannerly for a man to stare at a woman's hindquarters, such staring is now perfectly proper and even commendable, assuming that the man is admiring the woman's tail.

M: 15 — Always hold the tail with one hand, pressing it against the thigh, when passing through a revolving door.

Q: 03 — Never handle another person's tail without her specific permission; if in handling another person's tail you should feel warts, furuncles, or other excrescences, pretend you do not notice them.

B: 22 — In dancing, because of the close proximity of the two bodies, there is a constant danger of embarrassment to both parties, chiefly from the action of the tail in leaping to the gay position. The new style in ballroom dancing is recommended — each dancer to hold the tip of his partner's tail with the right hand, thus maintaining both tails in the upright position.

It is perfectly proper, says the Appendix, for a wife to brush a husband's tail while he is shaving, preparatory to rushing off to his business. By the same token, the husband should attend to the needs of his wife's tail, if she asks it, during the time she is dressing for an evening engagement. This latter rule recalls that in former days a wife's standard appeal to her husband was to "zip me," whereas today her request is likely to be: "Dear, will you come and do my tail while I do my face?"

Having the tail "done" has now become part of

the language. Such expressions as: "I'm on my way to have my tail done" or "That charming man Jacques, across from the bank, did my tail this afternoon," are heard frequently nowadays.* In passing, let us note that tail culture has brought about the enlargement of most of the nation's beauty salons; after having the hair on her head "done," a lady proceeds to another room, stretches out face downward on a padded table, and has her tail done. Some of the larger barber shops have installed tail tables, but they have not been overly popular inasmuch as most men prefer to do the job themselves.

Since there are constant changes as well as additions to the etiquette of the tail, the Bureau of Manners and Morals has in recent years been sponsoring National Tail Week each year in April. The emphasis is largely on education of adults who may have become slipshod in their tail manners, growing away from the basic training they received in school. The observance of this special week has already be-

* The controversial Dewey-Marciano Bill, currently before the House of Representatives, would forbid any male beautician from ever handling a female customer's tail. Though there is much agitation for its passage, Washington observers predict its defeat because of concerted opposition by lobbyists representing the Association of Junior Leagues, the American Legion Auxiliary, the League of Women Voters, the Associated Garden Clubs of America, and the Girl Scouts.

The emphasis is largely on education of adults who may have become slipshod in their tail manners...

come commercialized, yet there is no question that it has become a healthy thing for the nation. It culminates in the annual pageant at St. Louis, where Miss Beautytail is selected.

In speaking of this great annual tail pageant it is necessary for us to mention the scandal associated with it in 1994. The rules of the beauty contest required that a panel of eight judges — four women and four men — select Miss Beautytail. It was further required that each judge should feel the tail of each candidate, for the purpose of determining hair texture, muscular development, and vibratory quality.

In the 1994 pageant Miss Idahotail was in the process of running this gantlet, passing down the line of judges and having her tail felt. A hush lay over the great auditorium as she reached one of the male judges, Ferdy Wisdom, the New York columnist. Suddenly the stillness was broken by a voice.

"Quit!" it said.

And then:

"Kuhhh-witt!"

And after that:

"Yuh eeeeeeeeeeeee!"

At this point Miss Idahotail leaped from the

platform, shrieking hysterically, and ran out of the auditorium. She was soon located in a back alley, sobbing and exclaiming, "The beast! The beast! The beast!"

Later that evening Miss Idahotail appeared on television and charged that Mr. Wisdom had handled her tail improperly. Furthermore, she said, it was common practice among all the male judges to caress and fondle the tails of the contestants rather than simply *feel* them for muscular development and so on.

"Every girl in the contest," said Miss Idahotail, "knows about it and talks about it and puts up with it. But I'm a girl with a proper upbringing, and a Sunday School teacher to boot, and by God *I* won't put up with it!"

Miss Idahotail's revolt, as mentioned, created something of a national scandal for a time and it became necessary for the producers of the pageant to adopt corrective measures — in subsequent pageants all eight judges have been women.

Returning to the Blue Book, we may note that much of the etiquette prescribed for the tail has to do with ceremonial occasions. There are instructions concerning the various positions and movements associated with cornerstone laying, presentation at the

Court of St. James's, the midnight ceremony of New Year's Eve, shaking hands with the President of the United States, the signing of a contract involving more than $150,000, saying grace at table, and so on. An example of the need for constant change in the rules may be seen in the elimination of that section which formerly dealt with tail procedures during parades. A whole complex code had been worked out for drum majorettes, as well as for all marchers, with emphasis on the patriotic position (upright and bristling), which was assumed as the marchers passed a reviewing stand. Now that we have an international agreement forbidding all parading of any kind whatsoever — an agreement which, we are happy to add, has done more to lessen international tensions than any other pact of the last hundred years — the entire section of the book concerned with parade etiquette has been eliminated.

A few of the churches favor individualistic tail maneuverings for their particular congregations. One denomination requires a slight swinging motion during standing prayers; another encourages a violent jerking activity while hymns are being sung. For the most part, however, a passive and relaxed tail — the badge of humility — is the accepted form for church services. One important exception in almost all churches is the part played by the tail at weddings.

In discussing weddings, let us first dispose of an episode in social history which, in the opinion of most thinking people, was both ridiculous and disgraceful. This was the celebrated wedding of Countess Myrtle Cavadanza and J. Moran DeGroot, two members of the International Set, Division II. In the planning of their wedding, they announced to the press that Mr. DeGroot would place a ring on his bride's tail rather than on her finger. They had the approval of the clergyman who was to marry them, but on the day before the scheduled ceremony his bishop intervened and forbade any such procedure. The countess and Mr. DeGroot made a personal appeal to the bishop, offering a compromise. They requested that he grant permission for a double-ring ceremony. The bride would hold her left hand up before her face, and have her tail sticking straight out behind. Mr. DeGroot would first place a ring on her tail, then place another on her finger. The bishop ordered the couple out of his office and announced that they could not be married in his church. Eventually they were wed in a televised civil ceremony in which no ring was used;

at the end, before kissing the bride, Mr. DeGroot draped a Hawaiian *lei* over her tail. All in all it was a disreputable performance. What makes it doubly shameful is the fact that this couple, soon after their marriage, moved into Division I of the International Set.

The two most commonly accepted tail practices now associated with weddings are (1) the whitened tail of the bride and (2) the two tail positions assumed by both bride and groom during the actual taking of the vows. In almost all formal weddings the bride's tail is whitened. The cosmetics manufacturers have perfected powders that cling to the tail hairs and these are used by the great majority of brides. There is, however, a more expensive treatment called "Bride's Spray" which comes in liquid form and imparts an almost blinding whiteness to the tail. It has the additional quality of being fireproof.

It must be acknowledged that both bride and groom should have complete command of their tails during their wedding. Any sudden leaping of the tail, or even a pronounced quivering, would be visible to everyone in the church (save only the minister and immediate attendants) and could be a source of great embarrassment. Once again we see the wisdom behind the teaching of tail control to our children. A refresher course is usually given both bride and groom during the two weeks preceding a wedding, with special emphasis on the tail positions known as "hymeneal point" — the rigid, straight-out-from-the-body position required during the period of about forty-five seconds when the actual vows are being spoken — and "nuptial hoist" — bringing the tail to the upright position as the clergyman speaks the words: "I now pronounce you man and wife."

The tail has brought important changes, to be sure, in wedding costumes. The train, which was so popular in former times, is seen no longer. The bride's tail collar is usually of silver filigree (a costly item but no more costly than some of the elaborate trains worn in the past).

There is no doubt that the tail has made the wedding ceremony somewhat more complex than formerly. If any illustration of this point is necessary, we may recall the famous wedding of Miss Clarabelle Bickel, heiress to the Bickel Flea Powder millions. Miss Bickel was married in the ballroom of her family's huge factory near New Canaan, Connecticut. She gave no public warning of the innovation she had planned for the occasion. But when she came down the aisle and took her position before the minister, the audience gasped. She had a tailbearer — a little girl delicately holding the tip of her whitened tail. As the ceremony began, the child let go of the tail and it fell into the proper position. When the moment came for speaking the vows, the little girl reached out and brought the tail to the customary straight-out position (matching that of the bridegroom, who maneuvered his own) and held it there for the required time. And at the proper instant, Miss Bickel's tail was popped into the upright position. Because of the bride's social prominence, the episode created something of a sensation. Most of those who witnessed it agreed that it contributed to the beauty of the ceremony, that Miss Bickel had done a good thing in engaging and training a tailbearer, and that the custom would spread quickly throughout the nation.

It did not spread. No doubt Miss Bickel's innovation would have caught on had it not been for the nosiness of a woman reporter from a prolabor newspaper. Through some conniving with the Bickel servants, the reporter found out that Miss Bickel's tail was lacking in vigor. Owing to an injury she sustained in her college days (the reporter said she fell out of a tree while drunk), she was utterly unable to hold her tail in a horizontal position for more than ten seconds, and she could not bring it to the erect position at all.* Her motive, then, in using a tailbearer, was one of necessity. She might have publicly denied that her tail was crippled, but she chose not to, and the public, prone to believe evil over good, subjected her to such ridicule that she finally renounced her citizenship and moved her residence to the Cameroons.

In retrospect it seems unfortunate that Miss Bickel's act went for naught. Many a weak-tailed bride goes to the altar today faced with the ordeal of conforming to convention, her whole attention concentrated on the tail movements she must perform without help from anyone. There are occasional instances in which brides have collapsed under the strain. Had it not been for the boorish attitude displayed by the public in the case of Miss Bickel, it would be possible and proper today for a bride with a feeble tail to have a little girl handle both the hymeneal point and the nuptial hoist.

* Among the other scurrilous charges made against Miss Bickel by this antagonistic reporter was: "She was eight years old before she learned how to wave bye-bye."

X I

No Business Like Tail Business

THE HUMAN tail no longer can be regarded as an unwonted novelty. It is now forty years old. According to the latest census figures there are approximately twice as many people under forty as there are over forty; in other words, twice as many people have tails as don't have them, and the gap is closing fast.

It is correct to say, then, that the human tail has ceased to be a laughing matter. Those of us who have reached maturity with our tails have, nevertheless, lived through a period in which many people seemed to think that the new extremity was created as a joke, or as the butt for jokes. The entertainment world was largely responsible for the vulgarization of the tail. This was true in television, in motion pictures, and in the theater. Indeed, the manner in which show business played fast and loose with the tail was the immediate reason for the establishment of the Bureau of Manners and Morals.

For our purpose it is sufficient that we examine the minor phenomenon that became known as the "switch song." This regrettable business was the work of the singing comedians, chiefly in television and on the stage. They found that by taking an established popular song, known as a standard, in which some part of the body was mentioned and substituting the word "tail" for that part of the body, they could wring large volumes of laughter and applause from their audiences. For example, one of them took the old ballad "The Curse of an Aching Heart" and changed it to "The Curse of an Aching Tail." In fact that particular ballad is said to have been the first of all the "switch songs." In no time at all the air was filled with the music of the old songs with slight alterations in the lyrics, designed to appeal to the streak of vulgarity which seems to lie just below the surface in even our most genteel and circumspect citizens.

The theatrical trade paper *Variety* later published a survey of this fad, listing some of the distortions of standard songs as follows:

> I Dream of Jeanie with the Light Brown Tail
> My Tail Belongs to Daddy

...the great popularity of the panel show WHOSE TAIL IS THIS?'

No Business Like Tail Business

When Your Tail Has Turned to Silver
Dancing Tail to Tail
Sweettail of Sigma Chi
With My Tail Wide Open I'm Dreaming
You're a Sweet Little Tailache
You Go to My Tail
Put Your Tail Around Me Honcy
In Dreams I Kiss Your Tail, Madame
Tails Across the Table
Be Careful, It's My Tail
My Tail at Thy Sweet Voice
Zing! Went the Strings of My Tail
With a Song in My Tail
Smoke Gets in Your Tail
My Tail Stood Still
I Got You Under My Tail

There were many others, of course, and the American public seemed to find as much enjoyment in hearing them as the comedians had in singing them. After a few months, however, came the popular revulsion against a thing that was being done to death. There was also the legal intervention of ASCAP, the song writers' organization. This group understandably made violent objections to the vulgarization of songs that were a part of American tradition and folklore. By suing every comedian who took liberties with the lyrics of a song, ASCAP soon brought an end to the practice. It is interesting to note that the members of ASCAP have, ever since, refrained from writing any songs in which the tail is mentioned. The organ that still serves them best is the heart.

In fairness to all the good and honorable people in show business we must speak of the tail's importance in other phases of entertainment. In the legitimate theater, for example, there have been quite a few successful plays predicated on the psychological problems growing out of the tail. One of the best of these, winner of several top awards, was *Extremity*, by Woodrow Stackelbeck, a drama of dream sequences in which a beautiful young Southern girl believed herself to be a tree porcupine. This production was tastefully done, with fine restraint, and reached a dramatic climax when the young lady, hopelessly in love with an earthbound porcupine from Texas and convinced that her tail was prehensile, tried to hang by it from the limb of a cypress tree, fell into the swamp, and perished. As one who saw the original company in *Extremity*, the author cannot forego saying that the play provided one of the truly great moments in the history of the American stage.

For the reason that they had their origin in the night clubs of the bigger cities, we may consider that tail readers belong to the entertainment world.

No Business Like Tail Business

These tailomancers, most of whom are women, are enjoying a great vogue at the present time and have been prospering for several years. They are able to determine character and personality traits with great accuracy by feeling the subject's tail, and they are able to foretell future events. A few cynics refer to them as "tail witches," but there seems no doubt that their divination is grounded in scientific principles. And against the negative bleat of the skeptics we have the statement of Dr. Luddington Forepaugh, the kindly philosopher of the Katonah Institute for Retarded Adults, who said:

> We need desperately to have something in which to believe during these trying times. Therefore I believe in tail readers.

The author of this study has, in the course of his research, talked in person with one of the most successful of the American tail readers, Selma-the-Incomparable, who maintains luxurious studios in New York, Washington, and Bippus, Indiana (the last named is the town of her origin, where her original studio is maintained as a sort of shrine).

Selma's clientele reads almost like a skimming of the top crust of *Who's Who in America*. Members of Congress, Cabinet officers, presidential advisers, the wife of at least one President, several top men in the financial community, various leading actors and actresses, at least one major historian, and quite a few of the uranium multimillionaires of the Far West consult with Selma periodically, or have their tails read by her assistants.

In discussing her techniques, Selma goes back to the medical principle which we have already mentioned — the fact that the tail is in direct communication with the brain.

"Reading a tail," she says, "is the only true way of reading the mind. It requires not only a great deal of skill, but a special sensitivity to certain irregularities, a sensitivity which is basically spiritual. Since it is spiritual, it is mysterious, so don't go asking me to explain the mysterious to you. The most important single factor is that of tail vibrations. I am able to feel these vibrations where others would take oath that the tail in question is steady as a hoe handle. Yet there is much more to it than that. The moment a client walks into my presence, I begin to observe his tail mannerisms. His tail is under constant surveillance throughout the reading. By the time I am ready to feel his vibrations (by the way, I use both hands) I have a fairly close analysis of his character. And after I have felt and interpreted his vibrations, I am able to tell him what he should do with himself — whether it involves investments, political actions, domestic decisions, lost wallets, and like that."

With some hesitation the author brought up the widely publicized case of Leda Collop and Trudd Pickering. These two public idols from Hollywood, it will be remembered, were married in Paris in a ceremony attended by tens of thousands of screaming fans. Eight women, three children, and two elderly men were trampled to death or suffocated in the crush. It was easily one of the most splendid nuptial ceremonies of all history.

The whole world knew that on the day before the ceremony Miss Collop had Selma-the-Incomparable flown from Washington to Paris in a chartered rocket ship. The beautiful young actress had been a client of Selma's for some years, and now she insisted on a last-minute reading to determine if conditions were favorable for the marriage to Trudd Pickering. Such was her faith in Selma that she also insisted that the reading be performed in public. The two met in the Place de la Concorde and Selma read Miss Collop's tail while an army of gendarmes threw up human barricades to keep back the crowds. At the conclusion of the reading, Selma announced to the populace:

The Age of the Tail

"I can assure this lovely young woman that circumstances are perfect for her wedding tomorrow. She has a noble tail, and a responsive one, and I congratulate her. Her tail tells me that she has found the perfect mate."

The mob roared its approval and the wedding was held the next morning as scheduled. But what happened? Two months later Trudd Pickering tried to throw his bride out of a window on the twenty-sixth floor of a hotel in Geneva. The marriage broke up in a tempest of bitterness and recrimination.

"What went wrong in the case of Leda Collop?" I asked, in a quiet voice, of Selma.

"It is necessary," she replied, "that a client be wholly sincere and cooperative. That little bitch has been going around making nasty remarks about me. Well, I don't mind telling you, for publication, that she has the most miserable, beat-up tail I have ever handled. Oh, it looks fine enough, but it isn't genuine. It's a capped tail and underneath all the phony plastic and fake hair is an unsightly jumble of skin and bone that looks as if elephants had walked back and forth on it. The truth of the matter is that after I handled her tail there in the Place de la Concorde, and felt no vibrations at all, I whispered to her that she ought to take off the covering and treat her tail

[134]

with a paste made of pine tar and fuller's earth. But I decided to be loyal to her, and so I made the happy announcement. You now know how she has repaid me. She set me and my business back at least five years. If I had only known, I'd have jerked her tail out by the roots."

There are ups and downs in every business, no matter how serene it may appear on the surface.

Another aspect of show business in which the tail has an important function is that of precision dancing. There are many groups of these dancers operating today in television and the theater, but none so famous as the Golden-tailed Rockettes — an outgrowth of the tailless Rockettes of bygone years. These girls, as everyone knows, are a marvel to behold. The beauty of their performance, according to their director, Gene Devlan, is attributable more to their tail control than to any other factor. Candidates for the Golden-tailed Rockettes are put through tail tests much more intricate than those employed by the Registrar's Office at Yale University. Mr. Devlan has been quoted as saying that if one girl in the formation of two hundred and sixty holds her tail one inch off the correct position, the whole effect is ruined. The girls are drilled for hours and hours at a stretch, maneuvering their tails back and forth and up and down until they sometimes reach such a state of tail weariness that they burst into fits of hysteria. It is from their organization, incidentally, that the home tail shaker was developed. This is a device which shakes and massages a tired tail, freshening circulation and restoring at least a partial glow. The first of these machines was patented by a young man who was keeping company with one of the Rockettes. He was employed in a hardware store and he got his inspiration from the machine which shakes cans of paint. Most of the girls say they would be unable to keep up the pace if it were not for their tail shakers.

In television there has been one other development worth noting — the great popularity of the panel show *Whose Tail Is This?* Producers of the program attribute its charm to the suspense element involved, and to the fact that the public relishes a close-up look at a prominent tail. The usual master of ceremonies and panel of wits take part in it. The celebrity is concealed in a large barrel with his or her tail sticking out of the bunghole. The barrel is wheeled onstage and the panelists seek to determine the identity of the person inside by shouting questions. The questions are answered by tail wags — up and down for "yes" and from side to side for "no."

According to the latest census figures...

No Business Like Tail Business

It is all quite amusing. The most hilarious single incident to occur on *Whose Tail Is This?* took place on that famous evening when Vice-President "Honest Bob" Glutter occupied the barrel. The panelists were getting nowhere with their questions when out of the wings stalked a large alley cat which apparently had come into the theater from a warehouse next door. The cat spied Honest Bob's tail, crouched, leaped, and dug in with both claws and teeth. There ensued a loud rattling and bumping and thumping about inside the barrel together with muffled howls. When the cat was finally removed and the Vice-President emerged from the barrel, he was scratched and bruised from head to foot, and he was yelling, "Who the hell done that! Let me at 'im!" When he was finally calmed down, and after he had learned the truth, he was a good sport about the whole thing. "I'm not a coward," he said, "but just place yourself in my position. I had no way of knowing what was happening to my tail. It felt to me like someone was pouring liquid fire on it." *

* Vice-President Glutter has been one of our most remarkable public figures. Once a middle-of-the-road newspaperman, he quit journalism and ran for the United States Senate at the age of thirty-two. In that first campaign he told the voters: "I'm the same as everybody else — I like money. I want to get a lot of it. I've not been able to get it in my newspaper job.

The Age of the Tail

We come, finally, to the freaks — people who are able to do extraordinary things with their tails. There have been quite a few of these. Seen frequently on television variety shows, for example, is the act billed as "William Tail and Son." The boy in the act, now about fifteen years old, is able to execute a flat curl at the end of his tail and balance a small apple on it. His father, William Tail, stands at the far side of the stage and with unerring aim shoots an arrow which cleaves the apple.

There is also Conchita, the dancer, with her remarkably clever tail. She is able to tie a knot in it, using only the muscles of the tail itself. She stands perfectly still in a graceful pose. The tip of her tail slowly turns back, forms a loop, dips down under the loop, comes up through it, and then with a snap forms the knot. She performs this feat several times during her dancing act and she has worked out an amusing conclusion. Just at the end of the act a handsome young man walks onstage. As he passes

But if you'll elect me to the Senate, I'll get the salary, and I'll get more. People will come to me and hand me big hunks of money for my vote, and the beauty part of it is, I won't have to pay any taxes on that money. I'll be honest with you. I want to better myself, and give my children all the advantages." From that time on, he was known as "Honest Bob," and his political success, in spite of his youth, has been spectacular.

behind Conchita her tail snakes out, knots itself around his tail, and she drags him offstage.

Among the few members of the animal kingdom having prehensile tails are the monkeys, the tree ant-eaters, the tree porcupines, the coatimundis, and the kinkajous. There are people, however, blessed by nature with powerful and adroit tails, who have had the patience to train themselves up to the point where they can hang by their tails from a bar or a tree limb. Thus far we know of only two men and one woman who have developed prehensile tails in this country and all three of these have been snapped up by the circuses. One of the men, calling himself Joe Kinkajou, is able to swing by his tail from the flying trapeze.

There remain among us some amateur entertainers who are able to perform specialized feats with the tail, just as there have always been people who could wiggle their scalps or turn their tongues upside down. These performances, however, have been limited to such feats as holding a highball with the tail, or picking up small objects from coffee tables, or turning a doorknob and opening the door. One usually sees such exhibitions at social functions.

XII

Stamina Is Not Enough

THE READER will recall that in the opening pages of this monograph we dealt with the soft-tail sports — babies born with tails in the time when tails were not normal. Now the situation is exactly the reverse. In rare instances today babies are born without tails, and go through life without them. There is no great stigma attached to this lack of a tail. In fact we have in our present civilization certain people who get rid of perfectly healthy tails, by amputation, in order that they may pursue a favorite sport without let or hindrance.

The principal sporting activities in which tail amputation is practiced are those involving horses, football, and skiing. Those participants who have had their tails removed have done so without reluctance, in a spirit of dedication — the same spirit which led the Amazons of ancient Scythia to burn off their right breasts, the better to draw the bow.

Almost every sport has had its individual per-

...Sporting activities in which tail amputation is practiced...

formers, amateurs as well as professionals, who have chosen to rid themselves of the encumbrance of a tail. In some cases it would seem to be a matter of custom rather than of necessity. Professional jockeys, for example, are inclined to flaunt their taillessness as a badge of their trade. Some racing commentators have pointed out, however, that it is ridiculous for a jockey to have his tail cut off since he customarily rides in a forward crouch with his rump thrust high in the air. For their part the jockeys argue that they utilize the crouch only during the actual running of a race and that, moreover, a human tail swishing around on a racehorse's back is distracting to the horse.

Polo players, as a general thing, have their tails removed even though they use the English saddle. Rodeo performers, particularly those who specialize in riding bucking horses, are tailless. Many Western riders, in fact, have undergone amputation and these include performers in the cowboy movies. The West has stubbornly refused to substitute the English saddle for the more elaborate cowboy type, with its high cantle, even though it means that a rider must stand in the stirrups if he hopes to escape painful discomfort or injury. In those areas where riding to hounds and jumping are popular sports, some socially prominent women have had their tails removed rather than give up the pastime.

At this point let us note that the human tail has added an extra fillip to the sport of harness racing. Here we have the tails of both the horse and the driver streaming out behind them as they speed 'round the track, creating an effect that somehow adds to the beauty and the excitement of the scene, especially on a moonlit evening.

The impact of the tail on athletics is nowhere more pronounced than in skiing (except perhaps in football). There was a time when more than five million American men and women indulged in this sport. Today most of the big ski resorts have closed down. The professionals, for the most part, have had their tails removed and some of the more enthusiastic amateurs have taken the same course. But the man or woman with a tail who undertakes to ski, without possessing championship skill, is almost certain to suffer serious injuries. One need only visit the surviving ski lodges to witness the damage that is being wrought. The die-hards who sit around these lodges in the evening have possibly the worst-looking tails of any other group in the country. Their tails look as if they had been cudg-

Stamina Is Not Enough

eled and hammered and walked on and chewed up, and those with fresh-made injuries carry their tails in bamboo splints and bandages. The tail has had no comparable effect on fishing and hunting. Until he has become adept at the sport, a fly fisherman wears a sturdy tail sheath which the hook will not penetrate; among those of sufficient skill, hooking the tail is as rare a thing as it formerly was to hook the buttocks.

Hunters have had to adapt themselves to a few new techniques. In stalking operations they must be careful to hold their own tails steady, lest they confuse their dogs. A hunting dog who sees his master feathering at the stern while he himself is feathering at the stern is inclined to lose all interest in the quarry and develop a grumpy, sulking disposition. The death rate among hunters in the woods has, of course, risen sharply. Many of them refuse to take heed of repeated warnings, and go into the woods without camouflaging their tails; consequently, a mere flicker of their tails is often mistaken by other huntsmen as the movement of a squirrel, a deer, a rabbit, a moose, or some other game. If the mistaken hunter is a good shot, the victim merely gets his tail blown off; but all too often the mistaken hunter is not a good shot. Every hunter should wear either a camouflage sheath or a bright red tail apron for his own safety.

There was a time in this country when college football was one of the most popular of all the spectator sports, but no more. Today the game is almost exclusively in the hands of the professionals, who have their tails amputated; and even then, public interest has dwindled for the reason that the players lack the skill of the old-timers, who proved themselves first in college before going on to the professional game. College football is not altogether dead, even though the Yale Bowl today is used only for evangelistic meetings and intramural squat tag. In recent years there have been but four college teams in operation each fall. These are Notre Dame, Southern Methodist, Ohio State, and Duke. All four of these schools have stoutly refused to give up football, even though they have to play each other several times each season. The decline in college football began in 1974 when the first students with tails began matriculating. College authorities refused to permit tail amputation for football, and no really effective method for preventing multiple tail injuries has ever been found. Players for the four surviving football schools likewise are not allowed to have their tails removed, but they do employ certain protective devices which are thought to be the best that can be had. The player's tail is encased in a silken padded tube which extends down the inside of the left thigh and is fastened to the pants. A rubber device quite similar to the old-fashioned noseguard (which had a rubber lip that was gripped in the teeth) is worn over the base of the tail and has been effective in holding down serious injury in that locality. Even with these protective measures, the number of players incapacitated by tail injuries is appalling and it is unlikely that the four schools will continue with football much longer. And with the professional game attracting smaller and smaller audiences, it seems probable that football will soon become a thing of the past.

The game of baseball has seen a few changes now that the players have tails, though nothing quite so radical as the introduction in 1972 of the two-platoon system, under which a manager uses one team of star batsmen and another team of star fielders. The slide for a base has disappeared. For a while base runners tried to develop new techniques in sliding A runner going down to second, for example, would reach back and seize his tail with his right hand, pull it over to the side, and then slide

in on his left hip.* Quite often, however, the short-
stop or second baseman covering the bag would
come down with his spikes and hit the tail, and the
maneuver became so hazardous that it was finally
abandoned.

The tail-balk rule in baseball has been in effect
now for three seasons. Many batters formerly
adopted the practice when standing at the plate of
wagging their tails back and forth, or jerking them
up and down, in order to distract and worry the
pitcher. In some cases the pitchers became so in-
censed at these antics that they began throwing deliberately at the batter's tail. Wild rioting broke out
in major-league parks, once in Cleveland and again
in Oak Ridge. After much argument pro and con
a new rule was instituted. A batter is required to
immobilize his tail when he is at the plate. If he
wags it and, in the opinion of the umpire, is wagging it deliberately, a tail balk is called and it counts
as a strike against him.

The younger umpires, incidentally, are among
those in sports who employ the tail for signaling purposes. Where formerly they used their arms, they
now use their tails to call balls and strikes. Switching

* Speaking of slides, they have long since vanished from children's playgrounds.

[150]

from side to side means the pitch was a ball. An abrupt rising of the tail signals a strike. A third strike is sometimes indicated by a violent whirling motion. A few sportscasters have ridiculed this style of signaling and one sports writer has suggested, with biting sarcasm, that the umpire squat down and brush off home plate with his tail, but these criticisms seem to have had no effect.

The tail has enhanced boxing as a spectator sport, while, at the same time, it has worked a severe hardship on the boxers themselves. They face each other in the ring with their tails erect and slightly arched; the upflung, bristling tail is their expression of supreme confidence, contempt, and murderous intent. And so long as a boxer escapes serious hurt and retains his confidence, his tail stays up. If he receives a staggering blow, however, he is likely to lose control of his tail and it will descend. One of the most common partisan cries from the audience today is: "Lower his tail for 'im!" Spectators (as well as handlers) are able to gauge a fighter's physical condition and the true state of his mind by the general bearing of his tail from round to round.

The boxers themselves have complained for years against the extra burden that has been put upon them. They favor amputation, arguing that decep-

[151]

tion is an important part of their game, but they
have been ordered to retain their tails and, in fact,
a fighter without a tail is forbidden to enter the ring
in most states.

The essential points on both sides of this dispute
were summarized recently in a television debate between H-Bomb Warwick, the welterweight cham-
pion, and Sugrue Binsford, the boxing czar. The
following excerpt from the transcript of that debate
clearly defines the argument:

BINSFORD: Now, H-Bomb, you know darn good and well
that the public is sold on the idea of tails on fighters.
The first job you got is to please the public.

H-BOMB: The first job I got is to cold-cock that louse
Murphy next Saddy. I'll lower 'is tail for 'im!

BINSFORD: Yes, I know you're keyed up about next Saturday's contest. But we're talking about tails and their
desirability.

H-BOMB: Their what?

BINSFORD: Their desirability. You know very well that
when you enter the ring next Saturday, the audience
is going to have its eyes fastened on your tail. You
admit that, don't you?

H-BOMB: Cert-nee I admit it. They'll be lookin' my tail
an' they won't be lookin' my fiss an' they won't see
me cold-cock that louse Murphy. Why don't they
put boxin' gloves on the enna our tails insteada on
our fiss? Fightin' is with the fiss. Time I become

Stamina Is Not Enough

champeen, nobody knowed if I kayoed Vickers with my right or my leff or budded him with my head or bit him in the troat or what. You got everbody lookin' at your tail, who sees the fight?

BINSFORD: The fact remains that the public likes to watch the tails so they can tell if a boxer is weakening or not. I think it goes back to the days of cock fighting when . . .

H-BOMB: I'm sure gonna cold-cock that Murphy Saddy night!

BINSFORD: . . . back to the days when there was a basic sort of fascination to the sport of cock fighting. To-day's fighters do perform somewhat like a pair of banty roosters as they circle about the ring. The people like it. And the customer's always right.

H-BOMB: Yeh. All them lugs out the audience got to be wise guys, got to be smart. But who's the one got to be smart? Me. I got to do the impossible. I got to think about two things all at once. I got to think about that louse that's tryin' to cold-cock me, and I got to think about my tail. I got to keep that tail up. So I put my mind on that tail and keepin' it up and I ain't able to think no more about this louse, and this louse he cold-cocks me. You leave me amputate my tail off so's I don't have to think about it, and watch me cold-cock that louse Murphy in the first round next Saddy night.

BINSFORD: You'll do all right against Murphy, tail or no tail. I don't mind telling you, off the record, I got a substantial bet going that you'll take Murphy.

H-BOMB: Gee, t'anks, Commissioner!

The Age of the Tail

Thus the crux of the question as clarified by two of the leading personalities in boxing. While there is something to be said on each side, it seems clear that boxers will be required to retain their tails. It is worth noting that the biggest boxing crowds in the last two years have been those attending the fights in which Kid Ecuador has participated. And these crowds have turned out for the pleasure they get from watching Ecuador throw his celebrated "tail bolo." This is a long overhand right to the top of his opponent's head, accompanied by a rapid rotation of the Kid's tail so that it looks like an electric fan.

The importance of tail posture also applies today in golf. The key to good golfing, as is well known, is the relaxed manner. The amateur performer would do well to study the stance of the professional. As he addresses the ball his tail hangs as though it were dead. It continues in this relaxed position through his swing. Only after the ball has left the club head does any movement occur in his tail. If he knows instantly that his shot has been a good one, his tail will likely rise to the "commendable pride," or straight-out, position. If he sinks a long putt, he may rotate his tail in a clockwise direction to signify his extreme joy.

Stamina Is Not Enough

In the realm of sports there is one other feat that needs recounting in our brief survey. We have reference to the brilliant performance of the American girl Hazel Bonesteel. In the summer of 1992 Miss Bonesteel became the first person to swim the English Channel without once getting the tip of her tail wet. She covered nineteen miles and was in the water seventeen hours and forty-four minutes and never once allowed her tail to go completely below the surface. When she came ashore at Cape Griz Nez and was asked about her physical condition, she said: "My body feels strong but my tail is sure pooped."

XIII

Whither the New Member?

THUS we arrive at the end of this modest interim report on the human tail. The author hopes that his brief survey will serve future historians when the time comes for a definitive work on the subject. If there are flaws in this study, the author truly regrets them. He has made every effort to be objective. But the tail is still young and its impact on society is a continuing thing. By the year 2060 there will be a few aged persons scattered over the globe whose distinction, in addition to their years, will be the fact that they are the last of the tailless ones. Then they will be gone, and after that the time will have come for a comprehensive history of the tail.

During those intervening years, what will happen to add to the story? We can only speculate. Let us hope that mankind will not discover methods for using his tail as a weapon, as the monitor lizard and the sting ray use it.

Whither the New Member?

Whither the New Member?

Insofar as its physical proportions are concerned, it would appear that the human tail has stabilized itself. Yet there are some physiologists who suspect that nature is not yet finished with the tail. They say: "All things have a purpose. Surely nature had a purpose in giving us tails. We do not yet know what that purpose may be. There will probably be a further evolution that may take centuries, but in the end we will know the answer to the question. The tail will have meaning."

One group believes that ultimately the tail will become enlarged to serve as a storehouse for food. These men point to the Gila monster and certain kinds of sheep which store up fat in their tails against the coming of drought and famine. Perhaps the human tail will some day serve such a purpose.

Since we do not know, let us be content with the tail as it is. Let us recognize it as an important and valuable acquisition. It has brought additional beauty to the world. It has been the instrument for creating new wealth. It has served to improve the morals and the manners of mankind.

In a word, it has added luster to the human story and, best of all, illuminated one of our most cherished concepts — the essential dignity of man.